SALTERS ADVANCED CHEMISTRY

A2

Revise
Chemistry for Salters

Dave Newton, Chris Otter,
Kay Stephenson, Alasdair Thorpe

www.heinemann.co.uk

✓ Free online support
✓ Useful weblinks
✓ 24 hour online ordering

01865 888080

OCR
RECOGNISING ACHIEVEMENT

Heinemann

In Exclusive Partnership

Heinemann is an imprint of Pearson Education Limited, a company incorporated in England and Wales, having its registered office at Edinburgh Gate, Harlow, Essex, CM20 2JE. Registered company number: 872828

www.heinemann.co.uk

Heinemann is a registered trademark of Pearson Education Limited

Text © Dave Newton, Alasdair Thorpe, University of York 2009

First published 2004
This edition published 2009

13 12 11 10 09
10 9 8 7 6 5 4 3 2

British Library Cataloguing in Publication Data is available from the British Library on request.

ISBN 978 0 435 63155 0

Edited by Tony Clappison
Designed, produced, illustrated and typeset by Wearset Limited, Boldon, Tyne and Wear
Original illustrations © Pearson Education Limited 2009
Cover design by Wearset Limited, Boldon, Tyne and Wear
Cover photo/illustration © NASA/Science Photo Library
Printed in Malaysia , CTP-KHL

Websites

The websites used in this book were correct and up-to-date at the time of publication. It is essential for tutors to preview each website before using it in class so as to ensure that the URL is still accurate, relevant and appropriate. We suggest that tutors bookmark useful websites and consider enabling students to access them through the school/college intranet.

Contents

Exam hints and tips

Here are some general points that apply to both Unit F334 (Chemistry of Materials) and Unit F335 (Chemistry by Design) written exam papers.

1. **All the questions are structured.** This means that you are given a 'stem' of information that provides the context (the *Storyline*) for the question. This is followed by a series of part-questions. It can be quite helpful to underline key pieces of information as you read through the stem.

2. **The questions are designed so that you work through them in stages.** Answers to the part-questions are often linked together and are linked to the information you are given. There may be additional 'mini-stems' leading into a group of part-questions. So, remember to look back at both the information in the stem and your earlier answers. Work through the questions in order – don't cherry pick.

3. **Part-questions are linked by the context** – not by chemical topic. You may need to dip into several different parts of your knowledge in one question.

4. **Contexts will be a mixture of familiar ones from the *Storylines* and unfamiliar ones.** Don't panic if the context is unfamiliar – the chemistry you are being asked about will be familiar.

5. **The Data Sheet provides additional information not given in the question.** Make sure you are familiar with what is on the Data Sheet and remember to use it.

6. **All questions are compulsory – you have no choice.** Try to answer every question. It is better to make a sensible guess, which could score you 1 mark, than to put nothing at all. You cannot get negative marks. You have nothing to lose by guessing – so use your chemical common sense!

7. **Examiners use an agreed mark scheme.** The marks are given for very specific points, so you must be precise and use language (especially scientific language) accurately. Credit will always be given for correct chemistry, clearly explained or described, that answers the question that has been asked.

8. **Some questions will require knowledge of applications of chemistry and 'How Science Works'.** It is a good idea to have read and made notes on the *Storyline* sections listed in the 'Check your knowledge and understanding' activities at the end of each teaching module, as well as the *Chemical Ideas* you need. The spider diagrams, at the beginning of each module in this book, indicate clearly where there is *Storyline* content to be revised.

9. **The first question on a written paper is designed to be quite straightforward** to help settle you into the exam. You are advised to do the questions in the order they are set.

10. **Both Units F334 and F335 have synoptic content.** Parts of some questions use a wide range of chemistry drawn from across the two years of the course. Each teaching module in this book has an introductory page consisting of a spider diagram, which summarises the areas covered in that module. Some of these areas are highlighted in *italics* – these are areas previously covered in the course. They are indicators that this material may be incorporated into a synoptic question. There are also lists of the synoptic content on page 39 for F334 and on page 82 for F335.

What follows next are points that apply to F334 and F335 written exam papers.

Calculations

- Always show your working. Examiners use 'consequential marking' where possible so that they give credit for correct working, even if your final answer is wrong – so make sure you include everything. Even simple things, like calculating numbers of moles or relative molecular masses, can get you a mark.

- Write your final answer on the answer line, where provided.
- Always give units (unless already present) and a sign if appropriate (a sign is *always* needed for enthalpy and entropy changes).
- Give the answer to the same number of significant figures as the data with the lowest number of significant figures quoted in the question (this is usually 2 or 3).
- Always think about whether your answer is sensible or not – for example, ΔH_c values are always negative.

Chemical tips

- Give oxidation states with a sign – you must write '+' or '−' before the number (e.g. +3, −5).
- Enthalpy and entropy changes **must** have a sign as well as a unit (e.g. $\Delta H = +542\,kJ\,mol^{-1}$). Remember: sign, number and unit.
- Give state symbols in chemical equations only when requested. They are often asked for in reactions where there is a change of state.
- Use chemical language correctly – for example, make sure you know the difference between atom, molecule and ion; between chlorine and chloride; and between hydroxide and hydroxyl.
- Know the differences between molecular, structural, full structural, skeletal and 3D formulae.

$C_3H_6O_2$	C_2H_5COOH	full structural formula	skeletal formula	3 dimensional formula
molecular formula	shortened structural formula			

- Draw dot–cross diagrams properly, showing only outer shell electrons – and not forgetting lone pairs of electrons, e.g.

Diagrams

- Make sure that lines on diagrams are clear and unambiguous, and not 'sketchy'.
- Use a pencil and always label clearly.
- For experimental work, draw cross-section diagrams, not 3D.
- Check that any joints you have drawn look airtight and that there is an unobstructed path through the apparatus for any liquid or vapour. Think whether the apparatus *as a whole* should be airtight or not – for example, heated equipment, such as apparatus for heating under reflux or carrying out a distillation, must be open to the air at one end.
- Use an arrow labelled 'heat' to represent a Bunsen burner.

For more details of the experimental techniques that you could be examined on see pages vi and vii.

Quality of written communication

Both written exams will have marks for the quality of written communication (QWC) in some sections of extended writing. It will be made clear which answers are to be marked for QWC. To obtain these marks you need to:

- write legibly with accurate spelling, punctuation and grammar
- use an appropriate style of writing
- make it clear how ideas are connected, using the correct specialist language.

Experimental techniques

Make sure you are familiar with the following experimental techniques, as well as those used at AS. More information on all these techniques can be found in **Chemical Ideas Appendix 1**, **Experimental Techniques**.

Using a colorimeter (see Activity SS1.2)

For more information on what causes colour see page 38.

This technique is used to find the concentration of a coloured solution.
1   Select a filter with the complementary colour to the solution being tested.
2   Zero the colorimeter using a tube/cuvette of distilled water.
3   Make a series of solutions of known concentration, above and below that of the unknown sample. Measure the absorbance of each solution and plot a calibration curve (absorbance against concentration).
4   Measure the absorbance of the unknown solution. Read off its concentration on the calibration curve.

Thin-layer chromatography (see Activities WM5.1, MR2.3 and TL2.3 and Chemical Ideas 7.3)

This technique can also be used to follow the progress of a reaction. A reaction mixture can be sampled at regular time intervals. Initially there will only be spot(s) for the reactant(s). As the reaction progresses, spots will be observed for any product(s) formed. The reaction is complete when a reactant spot is no longer seen.

This technique allows the identification of components in a small amount of mixture.
1   Spot any mixtures and reference samples on a pencil line 1 cm from the bottom end of a t.l.c. plate.
2   Place the t.l.c. plate in a beaker containing solvent, making sure the solvent is below the pencil line. Cover the beaker with a watch glass or some cling film.
3   Remove the t.l.c. plate when the solvent is near the top. Mark how far the solvent had reached.
4   Allow the t.l.c. plate to dry. Locate any spots with a suitable locating agent – such as iodine or ninhydrin (for amino acids) – or reveal them under an ultraviolet lamp.
5   Find the R_f value for each spot: $R_f = \dfrac{\text{distance moved by spot}}{\text{distance moved by solvent}}$
6   Compare the R_f value(s) for your unknown sample to those of your reference sample/s to decide what the unknown is.

When carried out on silica plates, this technique is called t.l.c. When paper is used instead of a silica plate the technique is called paper chromatography.

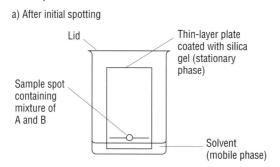

a) After initial spotting

Lid

Thin-layer plate coated with silica gel (stationary phase)

Sample spot containing mixture of A and B

Solvent (mobile phase)

b) After running a chromatogram

Solvent front

Separated components of mixture

○ B

○ A

Heating under reflux (see Activity MR2.3)

There are details on how to draw a diagram for heating under reflux in *Revise AS Chemistry for Salters* page vii.

1   Put the reactants in a pear-shaped or round-bottomed flask. Add a few anti-bumping granules. Attach a condenser vertically to the flask as shown in the diagram. Do NOT stopper.
2   Connect the condenser to the water supply.
3   Heat so that the liquid boils gently, using a Bunsen burner or heating mantle.

Recrystallisation (see Activities WM5.1 and MR2.3)

This technique is used to purify an organic solid with small amounts of impurities.

1 Dissolve the solid in a *minimum volume* of *hot* solvent.
2 Filter, and retain the filtrate.
3 Allow the filtrate to cool until crystals form.
4 Collect the crystals by vacuum filtration. Wash with a *minimum volume* of *cold* solvent.
5 Dry in air, in an oven set at below the melting point of the crystals or in a desiccator.

> A good solvent for recrystallisation is one in which the solid to be recrystallised is insoluble at low temperatures but very soluble at high temperatures. The solution is saturated when hot, and on cooling the substance crystallises out leaving impurities in solution.

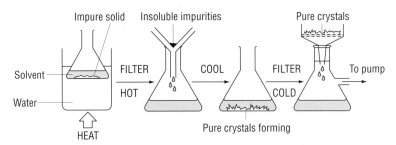

Standard electrode potential (see Activities SS3.1 and SS3.2)

This technique can also be used to find standard electrode potentials.

1 Construct the half-cell whose electrode potential you wish to measure. Ensure that all solutions have concentration 1.0 mol dm^{-3} and are at 25 °C.
2 Connect the half-cell to a standard hydrogen half-cell or other reference cell (see diagram) using a high-resistance voltmeter and salt bridge.
3 Check that the reading on the voltmeter is positive – if it is then the half-cell connected to the positive terminal is the positive electrode.
4 Record the voltmeter reading – this is the cell e.m.f. (E_{cell}).
5 Standard electrode potentials, $E^{\ominus}$, can be measured by connecting any half-cell to a standard hydrogen half-cell.

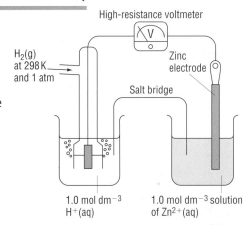

Carrying out an organic preparation (see Activities ES6.3 and WM5.1)

There are usually three stages in preparing an organic compound:

- reaction
- extraction of product
- purification of product.

After purification the product is often analysed for purity.

Organic preparations usually involve a range of experimental techniques. Those used most commonly are:

- heating under reflux (reaction)
- using a separating funnel (extraction)
- vacuum or gravity filtration (extraction)
- distillation (purification)
- recrystallisation (purification)
- paper and t.l.c. (purification and/or analysis).

Product purity can be tested by measurement of melting or boiling points, or by use of an appropriate titration.

> Sometimes, reaction mixtures or products may need to be dried. The addition of *anhydrous* sodium sulfate will do this.

> You can find out more about redox titrations on page 34.

> You can remind yourself of the detail of techniques not given in this book (such as acid–base titrations, distillation and reflux) by looking at *Revise AS Chemistry for Salters*, pages vi and vii.

How to use this revision guide

This revision guide is designed to support the OCR Chemistry B (Salters) A2 course, and is valid for the revised specification for first teaching in September 2009, with the first F334 examinations taken from January 2010. From June 2010, you may take both written examinations in January or June, or just in June at the end of the A2 course.

This guide covers the two written examinations for the A2 course, **Unit F334: Chemistry of Materials** and **Unit F335: Chemistry by Design**.

The table below shows the scheme of assessment for the A2 course. This enables you to see how the examination units and teaching content link together.

Examination Unit	Unit title and teaching modules covered	Duration	Number of marks	Mode of assessment	% of total Advanced GCE marks*
F334	**Chemistry of Materials** (What's in a Medicine?, The Materials Revolution, The Thread of Life, The Steel Story)	1½ hours	90	Written examination (synoptic)	15%
F335	**Chemistry by Design** (Agriculture and Industry, Colour by Design, The Oceans, Medicines by Design)	2 hours	120	Written examination (synoptic)	20%
F336	**Chemistry Individual Investigation**	45 marks: not covered in this revision guide – your school or college will organise this assessment	Chemical investigation of your choice assessed by your teacher	15%

* The other 50% of the marks for the Advanced GCE come from the AS units.

A spider diagram at the start of each module shows how the concepts in the module are related.

Under each topic title in this book there is a summary of the content covered. It allows you to see which sections from *Chemical Ideas* and *Chemical Storylines* need to be revised for that specific topic.

Within each teaching topic, the material is divided into short sections of one to three pages. Each section usually revises one section of material from *Chemical Ideas*, and ends with **Quick Check questions** to help you to test your understanding. Shaded marginal boxes provide useful hints and deal with common misconceptions and errors.

Summaries of synoptic content for each of the two exam units are provided on pages 39 and 82.

Also included at the front of this book are sections on **Experimental techniques** and **Exam hints and tips**.

At the end of each Unit are **Practice exam-style questions**, along with helpful marginal comments to assist you in answering them.

All questions (Quick Check and Practice exam-style) are provided with full answers.

The Periodic Table of the Elements is provided on the inside front cover.

An index is provided at the end of the book.

What's in a Medicine? (WM)

This module introduces the importance of the pharmaceutical industry. It uses aspirin as a case study to introduce some important new organic chemistry. The module also explores how instrumental analysis (mass spectrometry and infrared spectroscopy) can be used to identify a compound. 'CI' refers to sections in your *Chemical Ideas* textbook. 'Storylines' refers to your *Chemical Storylines* textbook.

Note: Italicised and underlined text refers to work *first* met at AS.

Note: Storylines content that relates to learning outcomes (spec. statements) that cannot be found elsewhere is shaded.

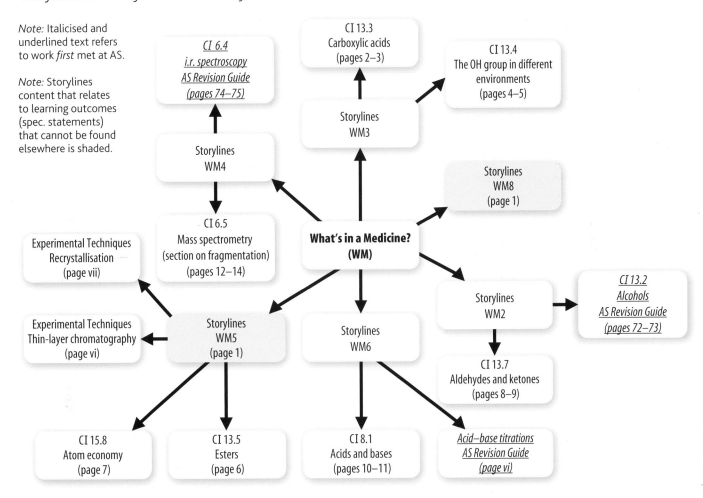

From *Chemical Storylines*, you also need to be aware of the development and safety testing of medicines (Storylines WM5 and WM8). If the structure of an existing medicine is altered slightly, this will alter its properties slightly. This means that when a useful activity has been identified, chemists will make many similar compounds (called analogues) to try to maximise the desired effects.

Combinatorial chemistry is the name given to a method for synthesising a large number of analogues in a short time. It is a technique used by pharmaceutical companies to make many related compounds in order to test them for pharmacological activity so that their potential as medicines can be assessed (see **Activity WM5.2**).

Once a potential medicine has been identified it needs to be developed. Three phases of clinical trials are carried out:

- Phase I trials establish if the potential medicine is safe.
- Phase II trials establish if the potential medicine is effective.
- Phase III trials establish if the potential medicine is better than the standard treatment.

Carboxylic acids and their derivatives

Chemical Ideas 13.3

This formula is often abbreviated to –COOH.

Carboxylic acids contain the **carboxyl** functional group.

Their systematic names all end with **-oic acid**.

When counting carbons in the longest chain to name a carboxylic acid, remember to include the carbon in the carboxylic acid group.

Name	Shortened structural formula	Structural formula
methanoic acid (one carbon)	HCOOH	
propanoic acid	CH_3CH_2COOH	
benzenecarboxylic (benzoic) acid	C_6H_5COOH	
3-methylbutanoic acid	$CH_3CH(CH_3)CH_2COOH$	
ethanedioic acid	$(COOH)_2$	

Note that this is 3-methylbutanoic acid and *not* 2-methylbutanoic acid. When naming branched-chain carboxylic acids, the carboxyl carbon is assigned number 1.

When two carboxyl groups are present the ending **-dioic acid** is used. Note how the *e* in the name of the alkane is left – e.g. *ethane*dioic acid.

Reactions

1 Acid–base reactions

To simplify things, chemists often say that acids produce hydrogen ions (H⁺) rather than oxonium ions (H_3O^+).

Being weak acids, carboxylic acids partially dissociate in aqueous solution to form oxonium ions (H_3O^+) and carboxylate ions ($RCOO^-$):

$$HCOOH(aq) \; + \; H_2O(l) \; \rightleftharpoons \; H_3O^+(aq) \; + \; HCOO^-(aq)$$
methanoic acid   *oxonium* ion   *methanoate* ion

Carboxylic acids react with bases to produce salts. They are important chemically because many useful derivatives can be made from them.

Remember:
acid + base → salt
       + water

$$CH_3COOH(aq) \; + \; NaOH(aq) \; \rightarrow \; CH_3COO^-Na^+(aq) \; + \; H_2O(l)$$
ethanoic acid   *sodium ethanoate*

2 Esterification reactions

Carboxylic acids react with alcohols in the presence of a strong acid catalyst (e.g. a few drops of concentrated sulfuric acid) when heated under reflux. This reaction (called **esterification**) is reversible and comes to equilibrium during refluxing:

For further information on esters, see page 6.

carboxylic acid +   alcohol $\rightleftharpoons$ ester   +   water
$$CH_3COOH(l) \; + \; CH_3CH_2OH(l) \; \rightleftharpoons \; CH_3COOCH_2CH_3(l) \; + \; H_2O(l)$$
ethanoic acid   *ethanol*   *ethyl ethanoate*

Tests for carboxylic acids

Although carboxylic acids are weak acids, they will react with carbonates to produce carbon dioxide.

Sodium carbonate or sodium hydrogencarbonate solutions are commonly used to test for acids:

$$2HCOOH(aq) \; + \; Na_2CO_3(aq) \; \rightarrow \; 2HCOO^-Na^+(aq) \; + \; CO_2(g) \; + \; H_2O(l)$$
methanoic acid   sodium methanoate

> Remember:
> carbonate + acid
> ↓
> salt + water
>   + carbon dioxide

The reaction will produce bubbles of carbon dioxide gas, which are readily seen and can be confirmed by testing the gas with limewater, which turns milky:

$$Ca(OH)_2(aq) \; + \; CO_2(g) \; \rightarrow \; CaCO_3(s) \; + \; H_2O(l)$$
cloudy
precipitate

Derivatives

Carboxylic acids are important chemically because many useful derivatives can be made from them.

Derivative	Functional group	Example	Name
ester	$-\overset{\overset{\textstyle O}{\|\|}}{C}-O-$	$CH_3-\overset{\overset{\textstyle O}{\|\|}}{C}-O-CH_3$	methyl ethanoate
acyl chloride	$-C\overset{\diagup O}{\diagdown Cl}$	$CH_3-C\overset{\diagup O}{\diagdown Cl}$	ethanoyl chloride
amide	$-\overset{\overset{\textstyle O}{\|\|}}{C}-\underset{\underset{\textstyle H}{\|}}{N}-$	$CH_3-\overset{\overset{\textstyle O}{\|\|}}{C}-N\overset{\diagup H}{\diagdown H}$	ethanamide
acid anhydride	$-C\overset{\diagup O}{\diagdown O}\diagdown C\diagdown O$	$CH_3-C\overset{\diagup O}{\diagdown O}\diagdown CH_3-C\diagdown O$	ethanoic anhydride

QUICK CHECK QUESTIONS

1. Name the following carboxylic acids:
   (a) $CH_3CH_2CH_2CH_2CH_2COOH$
   (b) $HOOCCH_2CH_2CH_2COOH$
   (c) COOH ... COOH

2. Draw the skeletal formulae of the molecules in questions **1 (a)** and **(b)**.

3. Give the equation for propanoic acid reacting with potassium hydroxide.

4. Which reactants are needed to make propyl butanoate? (Give names and formulae)

5. Draw the structural formulae of:
   (a) the methyl ester of butanoic acid
   (b) propanoyl chloride
   (c) propanamide.

6. When benzene-1,2-dicarboxylic acid (phthalic acid) is heated, it forms phthalic anhydride and water. Write an equation for this reaction showing the structural formulae of the organic molecules involved.

7. Benzene-1,4-dicarboyxlic acid and ethane-1,2-diol react together to form a polymer called PET. What is the general name for the type of polymer formed? Explain your answer.

The OH group in alcohols, phenols and carboxylic acids

Chemical Ideas 13.4

For further information on carboxylic acids, see page 2.

The hydroxyl group, –OH, can occur in three different environments in organic molecules – in alcohols, in phenols and in carboxylic acids.

Alcohols contain the hydroxyl functional group (–OH) attached to an aliphatic (non-aromatic) carbon chain. Some common reactions of alcohols were discussed in *Revise AS Chemistry for Salters* on pages 72–73.

Phenols are compounds that have one or more –OH groups attached directly to a benzene ring:

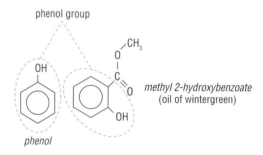

methyl 2-hydroxybenzoate
(oil of wintergreen)

Although phenols look similar to alcohols, their chemical reactions are different.

Test for phenols

Learn the name of the reagent used to identify phenols – this is a common exam question.

When **neutral iron(III) chloride solution** is added to phenol or its derivatives, a **purple** complex is formed. This test allows us to distinguish between phenols and alcohols.

Acidic properties of alcohols, phenols and carboxylic acids

Alcohols, phenols and carboxylic acids are all **weak acids**. They react with water, producing oxonium ions. For example:

$$C_6H_5OH(s) + H_2O(l) \rightleftharpoons C_6H_5O^-(aq) + H_3O^+(aq)$$

phenol   water   phenoxide ion   oxonium ion

The order of acidic strength is:

Ethanol is such a weak acid it is even weaker than water! The larger the K_a value, the stronger the acid.

	ethanol	<	water	<	phenol	<	ethanoic acid
K_a value at 25 °C (mol dm^{-3})	1×10^{-16} weakest acid		1×10^{-14}		1×10^{-10}		1.7×10^{-5} strongest acid

The strength of these compounds as acids can be explained by comparing the **stability of the anion** (R—O$^-$). Phenoxide ions ($C_6H_5O^-$) and carboxylate ions (RCOO$^-$) are more stable than hydroxide (OH^-) and ethoxide ions ($CH_3CH_2O^-$) because the negative charge on the ion can be **delocalised** across several atoms.

phenoxide ion   carboxylate ion

The difference in acidic strengths of these compounds is illustrated by their reactions with sodium hydroxide and sodium carbonate.

Reaction	Ethanol	Phenol	Ethanoic acid
Reaction with NaOH(aq)	No reaction	Reacts to form a salt $NaOH + C_6H_5OH \rightarrow C_6H_5O^-Na^+ + H_2O$	Reacts to form a salt $NaOH + CH_3COOH \rightarrow H_3CCOO^-Na^+ + H_2O$
Reaction with Na_2CO_3(aq) (and other carbonates)	No reaction	No reaction	Fizzes – CO_2 released $2CH_3COOH + Na_2CO_3 \rightarrow 2CH_3COO^-Na^+ + CO_2 + H_2O$

QUICK CHECK QUESTIONS

1 Draw the structural formulae of:
   (a) propan-1-ol
   (b) 4-methylphenol
   (c) ethanoic acid.
2 Which of the molecules in question **1** would:
   (a) give a purple colour with neutral iron(III) chloride?
   (b) react with sodium carbonate solution, producing carbon dioxide gas?
   (c) react with acidified potassium dichromate(VI)?
   (d) react with sodium hydroxide solution?
3 Write an equation for the reaction of phenol with sodium hydroxide solution.

4 Study the compounds A–C below.

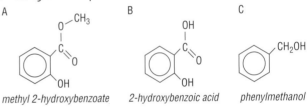

methyl 2-hydroxybenzoate   2-hydroxybenzoic acid   phenylmethanol

   (a) Identify the functional groups in each of the molecules.
   (b) Put compounds A, B and C in order of increasing acidity.

Esters

Chemical Ideas 13.5

Making esters

Esters are made by heating an alcohol and a carboxylic acid under reflux. The **esterification** reaction requires an acid catalyst – concentrated sulfuric or concentrated hydrochloric acid. The reaction is also called a **condensation** reaction and is reversible; it will eventually reach equilibrium.

$$CH_3-CH_2-OH + \underset{\text{ethanoic acid}}{\overset{O}{\underset{H-O}{\parallel}}C-CH_3} \rightleftharpoons \underset{\text{ethyl ethanoate}}{\overset{O}{\underset{CH_3-CH_2-O}{\parallel}}C-CH_3} + \underset{\text{water}}{H_2O}$$

ethanol ethanoic acid ethyl ethanoate water

The reaction can be reversed and the ester can be hydrolysed. In this case, a more effective catalyst is dilute sulfuric acid.

Phenols do not form esters in the same way as alcohols. However, phenols will react with **acyl chlorides** (at room temperature) or acid anhydrides (heated under reflux) to make esters. In both cases, anhydrous conditions are essential.

phenol ethanoyl chloride phenyl ethanoate hydrogen chloride

> The names of esters end in **-oate**.

Naming and drawing esters

> Take care to identify which carbons come from the alcohol and which from the acid. The group attached to the carbonyl group (C=O) is always from the acid.

Esters are named in two parts – the first part is from the alcohol (or phenol), and the second part is from the acid (or acid derivative) used to make the ester. You must be careful to get these groups the correct way round when drawing esters.

ethyl propanoate propyl ethanoate

Hydrolysis of esters

> Remember that with alkaline hydrolysis, a **carboxylate salt** is formed instead of the carboxylic acid.

Hydrolysis is the breakdown of a molecule by water – it is the reverse of esterification. The hydrolysis of an ester can be carried out using an acid catalyst (such as sulfuric acid) or an alkali catalyst (such as sodium hydroxide). Alkaline hydrolysis is usually preferred because the reaction goes to completion.

$$\underset{\text{ethyl ethanoate}}{\overset{O}{\underset{CH_3-CH_2-O}{\parallel}}C-CH_3} + NaOH \longrightarrow \underset{\text{ethanol}}{CH_3-CH_2-OH} + \underset{\text{ethanoate ion}}{\overset{O}{\underset{Na^+O^-}{\parallel}}C-CH_3}$$

ethyl ethanoate ethanol ethanoate ion

QUICK CHECK QUESTIONS

1 What are the names of the following esters?
   (a)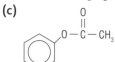
   (b) $CH_3C\overset{O}{\underset{O-CH_2CH_3}{}}$

   (c)

2 What reactants would you use to make each of the esters in question **1**?
3 Write an equation for the hydrolysis of methyl propanoate under alkaline conditions.
4 Explain why an esterification reaction is also known as a *condensation* reaction.

5 (a) Suggest how 2-ethanoyloxybenzoic acid (aspirin), whose structural formula is shown below, could be made in a one-step reaction, starting from 2-hydroxybenzoic acid.

   (b) What test could be used to show if all of the 2-hydroxybenzoic acid had been converted to aspirin?

Which reactions have the highest atom economy?

Chemical Ideas 15.8

Atom economy is calculated using:

$$\% \text{ atom economy} = \frac{M_r \text{ of useful product}}{M_r \text{ of the reactants used}} \times 100$$

If chemical synthesis reactions are to be sustainable, it is important that they have a high atom economy. Most synthesis reactions can be classified as one of the following types:

- rearrangement
- addition
- substitution
- elimination.

You can remind yourself about atom economy calculations by looking at page 52 of *Revise AS Chemistry for Salters*.

Rearrangement and addition reactions

No atoms are lost in a rearrangement reaction – they are just reorganised. So the atom economy will always be 100%. Addition reactions also have 100% atom economy because two reactants join together to form a single product with nothing else formed.

Rearrangement

pentane
$M_r = 72.0$

methylbutane
$M_r = 72.0$

atom economy $= \frac{72.0}{72.0} \times 100 = 100\%$

Addition

benzene
$M_r = 78.0$

hydrogen
$M_r = 3 \times 2.0$
$= 6.0$

cyclohexane
$M_r = 84.0$

atom economy $= \frac{84.0}{78.0 + 6.0} \times 100 = 100\%$

Substitution reactions

Substitution reactions involve replacing one group in a molecule with another. There are always two products formed, so the atom economy will be less than 100%. The larger the M_r of the leaving group, the lower the atom economy.

Substitution

$M_r = 78.0$

Cl_2
$M_r = 71.0$

AlCl₃ catalyst

$M_r = 112.5$

HCl
$M_r = 36.5$

$\% \text{ atom economy} = \frac{112.5}{149.0} \times 100 = 75.5\%$

Elimination reactions

Elimination reactions involve removing a group from a molecule. One reactant molecule forms two product molecules, so the atom economy will be less than 100%. Condensation reactions involve addition followed by elimination. They will also have an atom economy which is less than 100%.

Choosing the best reaction in a synthesis to give a high atom economy reduces the mass of waste in a process and is therefore important in potentially reducing any negative impact on the environment.

Elimination

propan-1-ol
$M_r = 60.0$

Heat
conc. H_2SO_4

propene
$M_r = 42.0$

H_2O
water
$M_r = 18.0$

$\% \text{ atom economy} = \frac{42.0}{60.0} \times 100 = 70\%$

Reaction types in order of decreasing atom economy:

- rearrangement and addition
- substitution and condensation
- elimination

QUICK CHECK QUESTIONS

1 Which types of reaction have the highest atom economy?
2 Classify the reactions below as addition, substitution, elimination, rearrangement or condensation.

Reaction A:

Reaction B:

CH_3CH_2 C CH_3 + HCN ⟶ CH_3CH_2 C CH_3

Reaction C:

OH

conc. H_2SO_4
reflux

+ H_2O

3 Calculate the % atom economy (to the nearest %) for each of the reactions in question **2**.

7

Aldehydes and ketones

Chemical Ideas 13.7

The names of aldehydes end in **-al** and ketones in **-one**. Remember that the carbon of the carbonyl group counts as one of the carbons in the chain.

These two homologous series both contain the **carbonyl group**: $\diagdown C = O$

This functional group gives similar chemical properties to both aldehydes and ketones. However, the hydrogen atom attached to the aldehyde carbonyl group gives some distinctive properties that enable the two types of compound to be distinguished. The names and chemical structures of some common aldehydes and ketones are given below.

$$\underset{methanal}{\overset{H}{\underset{H}{>}}C=O} \qquad \underset{ethanal}{\overset{H_3C}{\underset{H}{>}}C=O} \qquad \underset{propanone}{\overset{H_3C}{\underset{H_3C}{>}}C=O} \qquad \underset{butanone}{\overset{H_3CH_2C}{\underset{H_3C}{>}}C=O}$$

Preparation

You can remind yourself about oxidation reactions of alcohols by looking at pages 72 and 73 of *Revise AS Chemistry for Salters.*

Both aldehydes and ketones are easily prepared by oxidation of the correct alcohol. For an aldehyde, the reactant is a **primary** alcohol and the oxidising agent is acidified potassium dichromate(VI) solution, made by dissolving potassium dichromate(VI) in dilute sulfuric acid – the mixture is often abbreviated to $H^+/Cr_2O_7^{2-}$. Excess alcohol is used and the aldehyde is distilled off as soon as it is formed ('in situ') to prevent further oxidation to the carboxylic acid:

$$\underset{ethanol}{CH_3CH_2OH(l)} \xrightarrow[distil]{H^+/Cr_2O_7^{2-}} \underset{ethanal}{CH_3CHO(l)} + H_2O(l)$$

Warm, acidified dichromate(VI) can be used to distinguish between an aldehyde and a ketone. Only the aldehyde causes a colour change from orange to green.

If the primary alcohol is heated under reflux with excess acidified potassium dichromate (VI) solution, the corresponding carboxylic acid is formed (the equation is not balanced)

$$\underset{ethanol}{CH_3CH_2OH} \xrightarrow[reflux]{H^+/Cr_2O_7^{2-}} \underset{ethanoic\ acid}{CH_3COOH}$$

For a ketone, the reactant is a **secondary** alcohol:

$$\underset{propan\text{-}2\text{-}ol}{CH_3CHOHCH_3(l)} \xrightarrow[reflux]{H^+/Cr_2O_7^{2-}} \underset{propanone}{CH_3COCH_3(l)} + H_2O(l)$$

Remember – primary and secondary alcohols also give this colour change under the same conditions.

In both cases, the dichromate(VI) ion changes colour from orange to green as the reaction proceeds.

The dichromate(VI) ion is reduced to Cr^{3+} in the reaction:

$$\underset{orange}{Cr_2O_7^{2-}(aq)} + 14H^+(aq) + 6e^- \rightarrow \underset{green}{2Cr^{3+}(aq)} + 7H_2O$$

Reactions

Oxidation

Only aldehydes can be further oxidised with acidified dichromate(VI) because of the hydrogen atom on the carbonyl group:

$$\underset{ethanal}{CH_3CHO(l)} \xrightarrow[reflux]{H^+/Cr_2O_7^{2-}} \underset{ethanoic\ acid}{CH_3COOH(l)}$$

Aldehydes can also be distinguished from ketones by reacting them with **Fehling's solution**. The aldehyde is oxidised to a carboxylic acid and the blue Cu^{2+} ions are reduced to Cu^+ in copper(I) oxide. This forms an orange/brown precipitate. Ketones are not oxidised by Fehling's solution, so there is no colour change.

> Fehling's solution contains Cu^{2+} ions and alkali.

Reduction

The powerful reducing agent sodium tetrahydridoborate ($NaBH_4$) reduces carbonyl compounds back to the alcohol:

> This reaction is given on your examination data sheet.

$$CH_3CHO(l) \xrightarrow{NaBH_4} CH_3CH_2OH(l)$$
$$\text{ethanal} \qquad\qquad \text{ethanol}$$

$$CH_3COCH_3(l) \xrightarrow{NaBH_4} CH_3CHOHCH_3(l)$$
$$\text{propanone} \qquad\qquad \text{propan-2-ol}$$

Addition

All aldehydes and ketones undergo **nucleophilic addition** reactions with hydrogen cyanide in the presence of alkali. The cyanide ion, CN^-, acts as a nucleophile and attacks the carbon atom of the carbonyl group, which has a slight positive charge. The product of the reaction is called a 2-hydroxynitrile or cyanohydrin:

the cyanide ion
is acting as a
nucleophile

a cyanohydrin

This type of reaction is useful in organic synthesis because it produces a new C—C bond, adding another carbon atom into a molecule.

QUICK CHECK QUESTIONS

1   Name the following compounds:
    (a) $CH_3CH_2CH_2CHO$
    (b)
$$CH_3CH_2CH_2\overset{\displaystyle O}{\overset{\displaystyle \|}{C}}CH_3$$
    (c)
$$CH_3\overset{\displaystyle CH_3}{\overset{\displaystyle |}{C}H}C\overset{\displaystyle O}{\diagdown_H}$$

2   Give the formula and name for the alcohol that is oxidised to produce:
    (a) butanone
    (b) pentanal
    (c) propanoic acid.

3   What would you see if (a) butanal and (b) butanone were each warmed separately with warm acidified potassium dichromate(VI) solution?

4   (a) Draw the mechanism for the reaction of HCN with propanone.
    (b) Explain why an *alkaline* solution of HCN is used.

5   Give the name and formula of the product formed when $NaBH_4$ reacts with:
    (a) methanal
    (b) pentan-3-one.

6   What chemical test would you use to distinguish between propanal and propanone? What would you observe in each case?

Acid–base reactions

Chemical Ideas 8.1

Acidic solutions: turn litmus red, are neutralised by bases, have a pH < 7 and liberate CO_2 from carbonates.

One way of characterising acids is through their ability to transfer H^+ ions (H^+ is a proton). A base is a substance that accepts H^+ ions. This is the Brønsted–Lowry theory.

Acids donate H^+ to water in aqueous solution to become H_3O^+ (the **oxonium** ion).

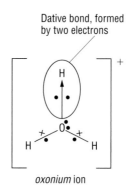

oxonium ion

An alkali is a base that dissolves in water to produce hydroxide ions – e.g. sodium hydroxide, potassium hydroxide and sodium carbonate. Sodium carbonate produces hydroxide ions by the following reaction:

$$CO_3^{2-}(aq) + H_2O(l) \rightleftharpoons HCO_3^-(aq) + OH^-(aq)$$

Proton transfer

An acid is a proton donor and a base is a proton acceptor.

In the reaction below, a proton is transferred from HNO_3 to H_2O. HNO_3 is acting as the acid and H_2O is acting as the base.

$$\text{H}NO_3(l) + H_2O(l) \rightarrow NO_3^-(aq) + H_3O^+(aq)$$
$$\quad\text{acid} \qquad \text{base}$$

Acid–base pairs

The conjugate acid is so called because in the reverse reaction it is the species that accepts protons.

In many cases, the donation of a proton by an acid is reversible:

$$\underset{\text{conjugate acid}}{HA(aq)} \quad \rightleftharpoons \quad H^+(aq) \quad + \quad \underset{\text{conjugate base}}{A^-(aq)}$$

In the equation above, HA donates protons and acts as an acid. A^- acts as a base in the reverse reaction. They are called a **conjugate acid–base pair**.

Depending on the circumstances, many substances can act both as an acid and a base. They are described as **amphoteric**. For example, water acts as a base in the presence of a strong acid, but acts as an acid in the presence of a base:

Just as all acids have a conjugate base, so all bases have a conjugate acid.

- Water acting as a base
$$\underset{\text{acid}}{HCl(aq)} + \underset{\text{base}}{H_2O(l)} \rightarrow \underset{\substack{\text{conjugate} \\ \text{base}}}{Cl^-(aq)} + \underset{\substack{\text{conjugate} \\ \text{acid}}}{H_3O^+(aq)}$$

- Water acting as an acid
$$\underset{\text{base}}{NH_3(aq)} + \underset{\text{acid}}{H_2O(l)} \rightarrow \underset{\substack{\text{conjugate} \\ \text{acid}}}{NH_4^+(aq)} + \underset{\substack{\text{conjugate} \\ \text{base}}}{OH^-(aq)}$$

Strength of acids and bases

Acids which are powerful proton (H^+) donors are called **strong acids**. **Weak acids** are moderate or poor proton (H^+) donors. A strong acid has a weak conjugate base, and vice versa.

Indicators

Acid–base indicators, such as methyl orange or phenolphthalein, are themselves weak acids. In order to behave as an indicator, the conjugate acid and base forms of the molecule must have different colours. In the case of methyl orange, the acid form is red and the conjugate base is yellow. If the indicator is represented as HIn, then:

$$HIn(aq) + H_2O(l) \rightleftharpoons H_3O^+(aq) + In^-(aq)$$

   red   yellow

If an acid containing $H_3O^+(aq)$ ions is added to the yellow coloured form of methyl orange, the equilibrium above shifts to the left and the colour changes to red. Similarly, if an alkali containing $OH^-(aq)$ ions is added to the red form of methyl orange, the equilibrium shifts to the right and the colour changes to yellow.

QUICK CHECK QUESTIONS

1 Identify the acid and the base in the following reactions:
 (a) $NH_3 + HBr \rightarrow NH_4^+ + Br^-$
 (b) $SO_4^{2-} + H_3O^+ \rightarrow HSO_4^- + H_2O$
 (c) $H_2SO_4 + HNO_3 \rightarrow HSO_4^- + H_2NO_3^+$
 (d) $HNO_3 + CH_3COOH \rightarrow NO_3^- + CH_3COOH_2^+$
2 In the reaction below identify the two conjugate acid–base pairs:
 $H_2SO_4 + OH^- \rightarrow HSO_4^- + H_2O$

3 Explain what is meant by the term amphoteric.
4 Classify the following reactions as acid–base or redox:
 (a) $CuO + H_2SO_4 \rightarrow CuSO_4 + H_2O$
 (b) $CH_3COOH + H_2O \rightarrow CH_3COO^- + H_3O^+$
 (c) $2FeCl_2 + Cl_2 \rightarrow 2FeCl_3$
 (d) $HCl + NH_3 \rightarrow NH_4^+ + Cl^-$

Mass spectrometry

Chemical Ideas 6.5

For details of how a mass spectrometer works and of determining relative atomic mass, refer to page 14 of *Revise AS Chemistry for Salters*.

Mass spectrometry is one of several techniques used by chemists to determine the structure of molecules.

Fragmenting molecules

In a mass spectrometer, molecules of the sample being tested are ionised using high-energy electrons or laser pulses. For example, if the sample contains butanone molecules:

$$CH_3CH_2COCH_3 + e^- \text{ (high energy)} \rightarrow [CH_3CH_2COCH_3]^+ + 2e^-$$

m/z stands for 'mass-to-charge ratio'.

The ion produced when butanone has lost just one electron is called the **molecular ion (M⁺)**. The molecular ion is often unstable and can break up, in a process called **fragmentation,** into other smaller fragment ions and uncharged fragments. The formation of the four major fragment ions for butanone is shown on the right:

Only the *positive ions* formed in fragmentation pass through the mass spectrometer to the detector.

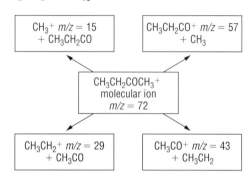

The mass spectrum of butanone ($CH_3CH_2COCH_3$) is shown here:

You can assume that all the peaks on a mass spectrum are caused by 1+ ions.

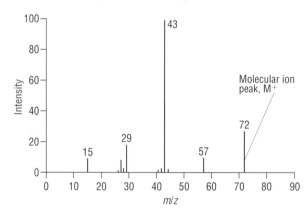

Beware! The molecular ion peak is often very small in size and the mass spectrum may consist of many fragment peaks, as well as the peak caused by the molecular ion.

A typical mass spectrum has the following features:

- the *x*-axis shows **mass-to-charge ratio**, *m/z* (*m* for mass, *z* for charge)
- the *y*-axis shows **intensity**.
- every line in the spectrum represents a **positively charged ion**. One line corresponds to the molecular ion (M⁺); the other lines represent fragments of the molecular ion or isotope peaks.

Interpreting a mass spectrum

m/z	Possible fragment
15	CH_3^+
17	OH^+
28	$C{=}O^+$ or $C_2H_4^+$
29	$CH_3CH_2^+$
43	CH_3CO^+ or $C_3H_7^+$
77	$C_6H_5^+$

STEP 1 Identify the molecular ion peak (M⁺). At low resolution, this is usually the peak with the highest *m/z*. This peak gives the **relative molecular mass** of the compound.

STEP 2 List the masses of the other major peaks (caused by fragment ions) in the spectrum. Then find the difference in mass between these peaks and the molecular ion peak. Some common peaks to look out for are given in the table on the left.

For example, for butanone:

Remember to put the $^+$ sign in when writing the formula of a fragment ion.

Molecular ion peak	A major peak is at ...	Difference in mass	Fragment responsible for the major peak
72	57	15 (i.e. loss of CH_3)	$CH_3CH_2CO^+$ or $[C_3H_5O]^+$
72	43	29 (i.e. loss of CH_3CH_2)	CH_3CO^+ or $[C_2H_3O]^+$
72	29	43 (i.e. loss of CH_3CO)	$CH_3CH_2^+$ or $[C_2H_5]^+$
72	15	57 (i.e. loss of CH_3CH_2CO)	CH_3^+

The largest peak is referred to as the **base peak**.

STEP 3 Identify any isotope peaks.

When molecules in the sample contain more than one isotope of any element, additional fragment peaks occur in the mass spectrum.

Some isotope peaks have *m/z* values larger than that of the molecular ion.

Molecules containing a single chlorine atom have an isotope peak at $M + 2$, caused by ^{37}Cl. Furthermore, the heights of the M and $(M + 2)$ peaks are always in a 3:1 ratio, mirroring the natural abundances of ^{35}Cl and ^{37}Cl. This is illustrated in the mass spectrum of chloromethane (CH_3Cl), shown on the right.

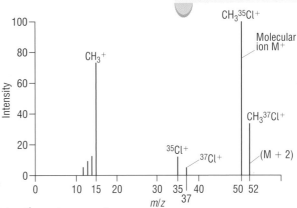

Any fragments containing carbon atoms will produce a small $(M + 1)$ peak, caused by the presence of ^{13}C. If a molecule contains only one carbon atom, the ratio of the heights of the M and $(M + 1)$ peaks will be 98.9:1.1. For a molecule with two carbon atoms the ratio will be 97.8:2.2, and so on.

In a sample of 100 carbon atoms, 98.9% would be ^{12}C and 1.1% would be ^{13}C.

WORKED EXAMPLE

The mass spectrum on the right is for an unknown compound P. The relative heights of the peaks at *m/z* = 120 and 121 are 100:8.8. Identify P and suggest the fragments responsible for the major peaks identified in the spectrum.

STEP 1 The molecular ion peak is probably the peak at *m/z* = 120. The peak at *m/z* = 121 is likely to be an isotope peak due to ^{13}C.

STEP 2 There are major peaks at 105, 77 and 43. The peak at 77 is almost certainly due to $C_6H_5^+$. The peak at 43 could be due to either CH_3CO^+ or $C_3H_7^+$. At this stage, two molecular formulae fit the data: $C_6H_5COCH_3$ and $C_6H_5C_3H_7$.

Molecular ion peak	A major peak is at ...	Difference in mass	Fragment responsible for the major peak
120	105	15 (i.e. loss of CH_3)	$C_6H_5CH_2CH_2^+$ or $C_6H_5CO^+$
120	77	43 (i.e. loss of CH_3CO^+ or $C_3H_7^+$)	$C_6H_5^+$
120	43	77 (i.e. loss of $C_6H_5^+$)	CH_3CO^+ or $C_3H_7^+$

The absence of peaks at *m/z* = 29 and 91 is further evidence that the compound is not $C_6H_5C_3H_7$.

STEP 3 The information about the heights of the M and $(M + 1)$ peaks suggests that the compound contains eight carbon atoms. This suggests the compound is $C_6H_5COCH_3$.

High-resolution mass spectrometry can produce molecular masses accurate to 4 decimal places. These can be used to distinguish between compounds that appear to have the same M_r values using a low-resolution spectrum. For example, a high-resolution spectrum shows that $C_2H_4N_2O$ has an M_r of 72.0323 while $C_3H_8N_2$ has an M_r of 72.0686. Extensive databases of high-resolution M_r values can be consulted to confirm compound formulae.

QUICK CHECK QUESTIONS

1 Why is it important to identify the molecular ion peak (M^+) in the mass spectrum of an unknown compound?

2 Draw a table to show the possible fragments and their masses (to the nearest whole number) in the mass spectrum of fluoromethane, CH_3F.

3 The most sensitive mass spectrometers can determine m/z values to 4 decimal places. The accurate molecular mass of a compound was found to be 43.9898. Use the following data to decide if the compound is CO_2 or C_3H_8. H = 1.0078; C = 12.0000; O = 15.9949.

4 The mass spectrum below is that of a common carboxylic acid.

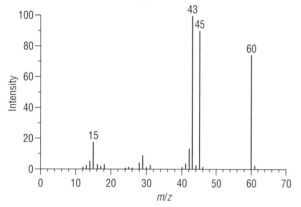

Identify the major peaks in the spectrum and find the formula of the acid.

5 The mass spectra of two compounds, A and B, are shown below.

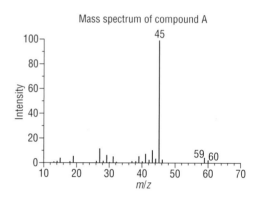

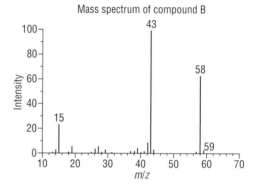

Compound A is converted into compound B when refluxed with excess acidified potassium dichromate(VI). No other product is formed. Identify the two compounds and account for the major peaks in each spectrum.

6 Sketch the mass spectrum for the compound bromoethane (C_2H_5Br). Identify the fragment ions responsible for each peak that you draw. (Note: Bromine has two isotopes, ^{79}Br and ^{81}Br, which occur naturally in a 1:1 ratio.)

7 Explain why the mass spectrum of chloroethene would have peaks at m/z values of 62 and 64. What would the ratio of the peak heights be?

The Materials Revolution (MR)

This module studies the development of materials with specific properties, with a special focus on condensation polymers such as nylons and polyesters. You will learn how chemists can change polymer properties by modifying their structure, and the issues surrounding the disposal of polymers. 'CI' refers to sections of your *Chemical Ideas* textbook. 'Storylines' refers to your *Chemical Storylines* textbook.

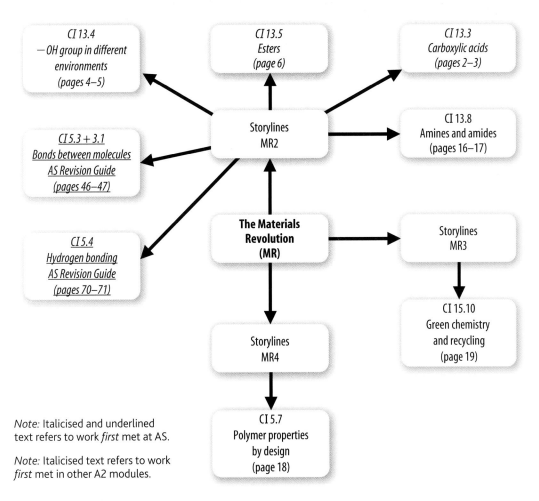

CI 13.4
— OH group in different environments
(pages 4–5)

CI 13.5
Esters
(page 6)

CI 13.3
Carboxylic acids
(pages 2–3)

CI 5.3 + 3.1
Bonds between molecules
AS Revision Guide
(pages 46–47)

Storylines
MR2

CI 13.8
Amines and amides
(pages 16–17)

CI 5.4
Hydrogen bonding
AS Revision Guide
(pages 70–71)

The Materials Revolution (MR)

Storylines
MR3

CI 15.10
Green chemistry and recycling
(page 19)

Storylines
MR4

CI 5.7
Polymer properties by design
(page 18)

Note: Italicised and underlined text refers to work *first* met at AS.

Note: Italicised text refers to work *first* met in other A2 modules.

Amines and amides

Chemical Ideas 13.8

The NH_2 functional group is called the **amino** group.

Amines are organic derivatives of ammonia. Ammonia has three hydrogen atoms bonded to a central nitrogen atom, whereas amines have one or more alkyl groups substituted for hydrogen. Like ammonia, the **lone pair** of electrons on the nitrogen atom is responsible for the three main properties of amines – they can act as **bases**, **nucleophiles** and **ligands**.

Lone pair of electrons

ammonia   *methylamine*

Primary, secondary and tertiary amines

A primary amine

A secondary amine

A tertiary amine

In **primary** amines, the nitrogen atom is bonded to **one** alkyl (or aryl) group. In **secondary** amines, the nitrogen atom is bonded to **two** alkyl (or aryl) groups. In **tertiary** amines, the nitrogen atom is bonded to **three** alkyl (or aryl) groups.

For amines with long alkyl chains, it is equally correct to use the prefix 'amino' followed by the name of the parent alkane, e.g. $CH_3CH_2CH_2CH_2CH_2NH_2$ can be called aminopentane.

Naming primary amines

Here are the names of some common primary amines:

- CH_3NH_2 **methyl**amine
- $CH_3CH_2NH_2$ **ethyl**amine
- $CH_3CH_2CH_2NH_2$ **propyl**amine
- $CH_3CH(NH_2)CH_3$ **2-propyl**amine (NH_2 group attached to the **second** carbon in the propyl chain)
- $C_6H_5NH_2$ **phenyl**amine

An aryl group contains a benzene ring with one hydrogen atom substituted, e.g. phenyl, C_6H_5-

Amines are bases

A **base** is a hydrogen ion (proton) acceptor.

Amines dissolve readily in water forming weakly alkaline solutions:

$$CH_3CH_2CH_2NH_2(g) + H_2O(l) \rightleftharpoons CH_3CH_2CH_2NH_3^+(aq) + OH^-(aq)$$
propylamine   *water*   *propylammonium* ion   *hydroxide* ion

The lone pair on the nitrogen atom forms a dative covalent bond with the hydrogen ion.

Like ammonia, amines can accept a hydrogen ion from water or from an acid:

$$CH_3CH_2CH_2NH_2(g) + HCl(aq) \rightarrow CH_3CH_2CH_2NH_3^+(aq) + Cl^-(aq)$$
propylamine   *hydrochloric acid*   *propylammonium* ion   *chloride* ion

Amines act as nucleophiles

A nucleophile is an electron pair donor.

Primary amines react with halogenoalkanes to form secondary amines, for example:

Nucleophilic attack at $\delta+$ carbon

primary amine   halogenoalkane   secondary amine   *hydrogen chloride*

The primary amine is acting as a **nucleophile**. It attacks the $\delta+$ carbon in the halogenoalkane. The secondary amine formed in this reaction can go on to react with another molecule of halogenoalkane to make a tertiary amine. Successive hydrogen atoms are being replaced by alkyl groups – this is an **alkylation** reaction.

Amines also react with acyl chlorides in an **acylation** reaction and the product is a secondary amide. For example:

$$H_3C-\overset{\overset{..}{N}}{\underset{H}{|}}-H + \overset{O}{\underset{Cl}{\overset{||}{C}}}{}^{\delta\pm}CH_3 \longrightarrow H_3C-\overset{\overset{..}{N}}{\underset{H}{|}}-\overset{O}{\overset{||}{C}}{}_{CH_3} + HCl$$

amine   acyl chloride   secondary amide   *hydrogen chloride*

Amides

Primary amides have the general structural formula: $R-\overset{O}{\overset{||}{C}}{}_{NH_2}$

Secondary amides have the general structural formula: $R'-\overset{O}{\overset{||}{C}}{}_{N-H}^{\underset{R}{|}}$

The polymer nylon is an example of a polyamide:

$$\left[\overset{O}{\overset{||}{C}}-(CH_2)_4-\overset{\overset{O}{||}}{C}-\overset{H}{\underset{}{N}}-(CH_2)_6-\overset{H}{\underset{}{N}}-\overset{O}{\overset{||}{C}}\right]_n$$

nylon-6,6

Hydrolysis of amides

Hydrolysis means bond breaking through reaction with water. When amides are hydrolysed, it is the C—N bond that breaks. The reaction can be catalysed by acid or alkali, leading to the formation of slightly different products.

> Acid hydrolysis gives a carboxylic acid and a substituted ammonium ion, while alkaline hydrolysis gives an amine and a carboxylate anion.

An example of acid hydrolysis is:

$$CH_3-\overset{O}{\overset{||}{C}}-\overset{\text{this bond breaks}}{\underset{H}{\underset{|}{N}}}-CH_3 + H_2O \xrightarrow[\text{catalyst}]{H^+} CH_3-\overset{O}{\overset{||}{C}}-OH + H-\overset{H}{\underset{H}{\overset{|}{N^{\pm}}}}-CH_3$$

amide   carboxylic acid   alkylammonium ion

Moderately concentrated acid (e.g. 4 mol dm^{-3} HCl, reflux)

An example of alkaline hydrolysis is:

$$CH_3-\overset{O}{\overset{||}{C}}-\overset{\text{this bond breaks}}{\underset{H}{\underset{|}{N}}}-CH_3 + H_2O \xrightarrow[\text{catalyst}]{OH^-} CH_3-\overset{O}{\overset{||}{C}}-O^- + H-\overset{..}{\underset{H}{\overset{|}{N}}}-CH_3$$

amide   carboxylate anion   amine

Moderately concentrated alkali (e.g. 2 mol dm^{-3} NaOH, reflux)

> Learn the reaction conditions and products for hydrolysis.

QUICK CHECK QUESTIONS

1 Name the following amines:
   (a) CH_3NH_2
   (b) $C_6H_5NH_2$
   (c) $CH_3CH_2CH_2NH_2$
   (d) $CH_3CH_2CH_2(NH)CH_3$
   (e) $(CH_3)_3N$.
2 Which amines in question **1** are
   (a) primary?
   (b) secondary?
   (c) tertiary?
3 Draw the structural formulae for the following compounds:
   (a) 2-aminobutane
   (b) 1,6-diaminohexane
   (c) propanamide
   (d) *N*-ethylethanamide.

4 Write equations for the reaction of methylamine with:
   (a) hydrochloric acid
   (b) water
   (c) ethanoyl chloride.
5 Complete the following equations:
   (a) $CH_3CH_2CH_2Cl + CH_3NH_2 \rightarrow$
   (b) $CH_3COCl + CH_3CH_2NH_2 \rightarrow$
6 Write equations for:
   (a) the hydrolysis of $CH_3CONHC_2H_5$ using an acid catalyst
   (b) the hydrolysis of nylon-6,6 under alkaline conditions.
   For each reaction, give the reagents and essential reaction conditions.

Polymer properties by design

Chemical Ideas 5.7

In **addition polymerisation** (see page 67 in *Revise AS Chemistry for Salters*) small molecules are *not* eliminated when monomers react.

During **condensation polymerisation**, two different monomers join together forming a **condensation polymer**. At the same time, a small molecule, often water or hydrogen chloride, is eliminated. Two common groups of condensation polymers are **polyamides** (nylons) and **polyesters**. Polyamides are made by condensing diamines and dicarboxylic acids. Polyesters are made by condensing diols and dicarboxylic acids.

How do temperature changes affect polymers?

The monomers must have reactive groups at both ends of a carbon chain.

At room temperature, most polymers have some **crystalline** regions (highly ordered chains) and some **amorphous** regions (randomly arranged chains). Cooling the polymer gives a higher percentage of crystalline regions. Eventually, the **glass transition temperature** (T_g) is reached and the polymer becomes brittle or glass-like. As a polymer warms up, the polymer chains slide over each other more easily, making it increasingly flexible. After continued heating, the **melting temperature** (T_m) is reached and the polymer becomes liquid.

The higher the percentage of crystalline regions the stiffer the polymer.

Bonds between polymer chains

Hydrogen bonding holds nylon chains together.

Permanent dipole–permanent dipole bonds hold polyester chains together.

The individual polymer chains are held together by intermolecular bonds. In general, the longer the polymer chains, the stronger the polymer – because there are more intermolecular bonds. Both nylons and polyesters form linear polymer chains, making them ideal for use as fibres.

Modifying polymer properties

You can revise the role of chain length on polymer properties by refering to page 68 of *Revise AS Chemistry for Salters*.

Chemists can lower the glass transition temperature by **copolymerisation**. Introducing monomers with larger side groups pushes the polymer chains further apart, weakening the bonds between them. Adding **plasticisers** also lowers T_g. Plasticisers are molecules that sit between the polymer chains, allowing them to slide more freely. We can increase the strength of a polymer by **cold drawing**. As the polymer is stretched, a 'neck' forms in which the polymer chains become aligned, giving more opportunities for intermolecular bonding.

QUICK CHECK QUESTIONS

1 Explain how a condensation polymer is made.
2 How does condensation polymerisation differ from addition polymerisation?
3 Poly(chloroethene) has a glass transition temperature of 80 °C. Describe and explain the properties of the polymer at
   (a) 40 °C   (b) 100 °C.
4 Explain how
   (a) copolymerisation and
   (b) plasticisers can be used to alter the glass transition temperature of a polymer.

5 Draw a section of the polymer chain formed when the following monomers react:
   (a) $H_2N(CH_2)_4NH_2$ and $HOOC(CH_2)_5COOH$
   (b)

6 What are the strongest intermolecular bonds between each of the polymer chains you have drawn in question **5**?

Green chemistry and recycling

Chemical Ideas 15.10

Recycling plastic waste

We generate vast amounts of rubbish, much of which goes to landfill. Although only a small percentage by mass is plastics, these take a very long time to decompose.

One alternative to burial is to **recycle** plastics, but identifying them and sorting different polymers from domestic waste is expensive. New technology to sort plastics automatically is being developed. Many thermoplastics are made from more than one type of monomer (copolymers) and may be suitable only for **remoulding**.

Another approach is to turn polymers back to the original monomers by **cracking**. The recovered monomers can then be turned into new plastics or used in other parts of the chemical industry.

A third option is to design **degradable** plastics. In the future, we could use more **biopolymers** (molecules made by living organisms such as bacteria or plants), synthetic **biodegradable** plastics or **photodegradable** plastics. All of these materials break down in the environment, although the speed of this process may still prove to be problematic.

A less favourable option is to burn the plastics, to release energy.

> European governments impose a landfill tax in order to encourage the reuse and recycling of materials.

> 'Process scrap' – scrap material from the plastics industry – needs little sorting since it is made up from mostly one sort of plastic. It makes up about 95% of recycled plastic in the UK.

Reducing carbon emissions

The energy consumed in producing a tonne of material by recycling is much lower than producing a tonne of the same substance from new raw materials. If less fossil fuel is burned, this leads to a reduction in emissions of carbon dioxide. For example, over 15 tonnes of carbon dioxide are saved for every tonne of aluminium produced from recycled metal.

It is now common to measure carbon emissions over the entire life cycle of a material. A 'life cycle assessment' measures emissions during the extraction of raw materials, the manufacture of the product, the distribution to customers and its eventual disposal. This 'cradle-to-grave' approach should allow chemists to evaluate better the impact of producing any material, and to design processes that have a lower impact on the environment.

> Burning plastics may cause environmental problems, such as increased CO_2 emissions.

> You can remind yourself about the principles of green chemistry by reading pages 50–52 of *Revise AS Chemistry for Salters*.

Minimising hazardous waste

'Green chemistry' involves designing chemical processes that reduce or eliminate waste and the use of hazardous materials.

QUICK CHECK QUESTIONS

1 Why is it easier to recycle plastics from industry than from domestic waste?

2 How is cracking used to produce new plastics?

3 Name three types of degradable plastics.

4 Explain the 'life cycle assessment' approach to carbon emissions.

UNIT F334

The Thread of Life (TL)

This module looks at the structure of proteins, the role of RNA and DNA in protein synthesis, and the ways in which proteins with special properties can affect our lives. The concepts covered are shown in the diagram below. 'CI' refers to sections in your *Chemical Ideas* textbook. 'Storylines' refers to *Chemical Storylines*.

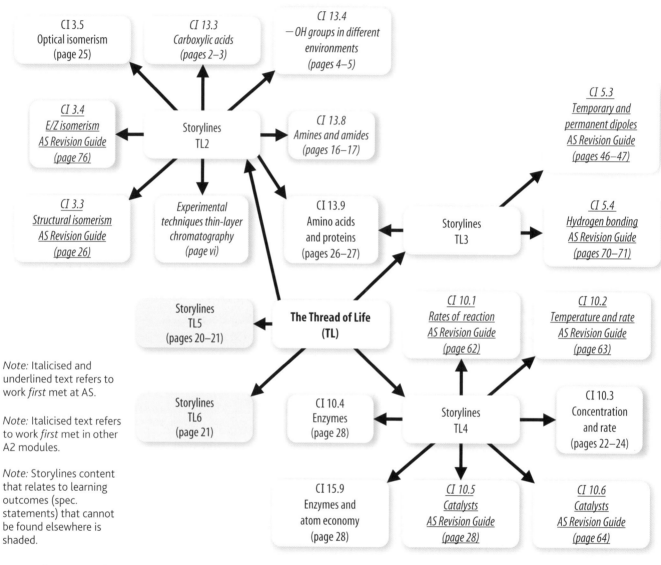

CI 3.5
Optical isomerism
(page 25)

CI 13.3
Carboxylic acids
(pages 2–3)

CI 13.4
— OH groups in different
environments
(pages 4–5)

CI 3.4
E/Z isomerism
AS Revision Guide
(page 76)

Storylines
TL2

CI 13.8
Amines and amides
(pages 16–17)

CI 5.3
Temporary and
permanent dipoles
AS Revision Guide
(pages 46–47)

CI 3.3
Structural isomerism
AS Revision Guide
(page 26)

Experimental
techniques thin-layer
chromatography
(page vi)

CI 13.9
Amino acids
and proteins
(pages 26–27)

Storylines
TL3

CI 5.4
Hydrogen bonding
AS Revision Guide
(pages 70–71)

Storylines
TL5
(pages 20–21)

The Thread of Life
(TL)

CI 10.1
Rates of reaction
AS Revision Guide
(page 62)

CI 10.2
Temperature and rate
AS Revision Guide
(page 63)

Note: Italicised and underlined text refers to work *first* met at AS.

Note: Italicised text refers to work *first* met in other A2 modules.

Note: Storylines content that relates to learning outcomes (spec. statements) that cannot be found elsewhere is shaded.

Storylines
TL6
(page 21)

CI 10.4
Enzymes
(page 28)

Storylines
TL4

CI 10.3
Concentration
and rate
(pages 22–24)

CI 15.9
Enzymes and
atom economy
(page 28)

CI 10.5
Catalysts
AS Revision Guide
(page 28)

CI 10.6
Catalysts
AS Revision Guide
(page 64)

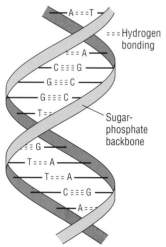

A===T
===Hydrogen bonding
===A
C===G
G===C
G===C
T==
Sugar-phosphate backbone
==G
T===A
T===A
C===G
A==

From *Chemical Storylines*, you also need to be aware of the following.

The structure of DNA (Storylines TL5)

DNA (deoxyribonucleic acid) is a double-stranded helix. The strands are made up from 'building blocks' of **sugar** groups (deoxyribose), **phosphate** groups and four different **bases** – adenine (A), thymine (T), cytosine (C) and guanine (G). The phosphate and sugar groups join together in a condensation reaction to form a 'sugar-phosphate backbone'. One of the four bases is joined to each sugar residue – again in a condensation reaction. The two strands in DNA are held together by hydrogen bonds between pairs of bases.

Adenine always pairs with thymine, and cytosine with guanine. This is known as **complementary base pairing**. Base pairing allows a DNA molecule to copy itself before cell division – a process called **replication**.

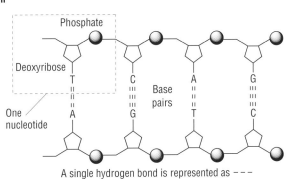

DNA chain

thymine

Hydrogen bonding between thymine and adenine

adenine

DNA chain

or   T ═ ═ ═ A

Several different models were proposed for the structure of DNA in the early 1950s. As different scientific evidence came to light, different models were proposed for the structure of DNA.

In 1953, Francis Crick and James Watson published their now famous paper in which they proposed the double-helix structure. They used X-ray crystallography data obtained by Maurice Wilkins and Rosalind Franklin to help support their ideas.

Phosphate

Deoxyribose

One nucleotide

Base pairs

A single hydrogen bond is represented as – – –

> The structures of the deoxyribose, ribose, phosphate and each base are shown on the Data Sheets which come with every examination paper.

> A **nucleotide** contains one sugar, one phosphate and one base joined together. DNA is a condensation polymer formed from nucleotide monomers.

> RNA differs from DNA in three ways – it contains the sugar ribose instead of deoxyribose; it has the base uracil (U) instead of thymine (T); and it consists of only a single strand.

> Make sure that you are familiar with the examination Data Sheet, including the section on protein synthesis in cells.

Protein synthesis (Storylines TL5)

The sequence of bases along a strand of DNA is the code for the sequence of amino acids in a protein. After unzipping the DNA, the code is **transcribed** into **mRNA** – this carries a complementary version of the code. mRNA passes from the cell nucleus to the cytoplasm where **ribosomes translate** the code – each three-base **codon** on the mRNA strand codes for one amino acid. Amino acids are brought to the ribosome by specific **tRNA** molecules and are joined together to make the protein chain.

DNA fingerprinting and ethical issues (Storylines TL6)

DNA fingerprinting is used to determine the probability that genetic material came from a particular individual (except genetically identical twins, no two people share the same DNA). The technique is used as a tool to help in solving serious crimes, to clarify immigration disputes and to establish paternity or maternity.

A DNA sample is obtained and is cut into fragments using a restriction enzyme. The fragments are then separated by size using electrophoresis. Each fragment is marked with a probe, and then exposed on X-ray film, producing a pattern of black bars – a 'DNA fingerprint'.

There are many ethical issues surrounding the use and storage of genetic data. These include issues about the ownership of genetic information and about genetic testing. You should be able to discuss the following issues:

Ownership
- Who should have access to personal genetic information?
- Who owns and controls genetic information?
- Who owns genes and other pieces of DNA?

DNA testing
- Should parents have the right to have their children tested?
- Should tests be performed for genetic diseases?
- Should an individual always be given his/her genetic information?

The effect of concentration on rate

Chemical Ideas 10.3

The units of rate of reaction are usually $mol\,dm^{-3}\,s^{-1}$.

What do we mean by rate of reaction? The rate of a reaction is a measure of how fast the reactants are used up or how fast the products are formed.

$$\text{rate of reaction} = \frac{\text{change in concentration of reactant or product}}{\text{time taken}}$$

What is a rate equation?

For the general reaction:

A + B → products

the rate equation would be rate = $k[A]^m[B]^n$ where:

Order with respect to reactant	Effect of doubling the concentration of a reactant on the rate of reaction
zero	nil
first	doubles
second	quadruples

- [A] and [B] are the initial concentrations of reactants A and B
- k is the rate constant for the reaction at a specified temperature
- m is the order of reaction with respect to reactant A
- n is the order of reaction with respect to reactant B
- $(n + m)$ is the overall order of the reaction.

Two examples of rate equations, and what they mean, are given below:

You will only meet values of m and n that are 0, 1 or 2.

$$CH_3COCH_3(aq) + I_2(aq) \xrightarrow{H^+} CH_3COCH_2I(aq) + H^+(aq) + I^-(aq)$$

rate = $k[CH_3COCH_3][H^+]$

The reaction is:

- first order with respect to CH_3COCH_3
- first order with respect to H^+
- zero order with respect to I_2
- second order overall.

Catalysts are not classed as reactants in chemical equations but they **may** appear in a rate equation.

$$(CH_3)_3CBr(aq) + OH^-(aq) \rightarrow (CH_3)_3COH(aq) + Br^-(aq)$$ **rate = $k[(CH_3)_3CBr]$**

The reaction is:

- first order with respect to $(CH_3)_3CBr$
- zero order with respect to OH^-
- first order overall.

Remember – it is the initial concentrations of the reactants and/or catalyst (not products!) that appear in the rate equation.

The effect of a temperature change on the value of k

The rate of a chemical reaction increases whenever temperature is increased. Since:

rate = $k[A]^m[B]^n$

a rise in temperature must increase the value of the rate constant, k.

Determining a rate equation

A rate equation needs to be determined experimentally. If more than one reactant is involved, a series of experiments needs to be carried out, e.g. for the following reaction:

A + B → products

- An initial set of reactions is carried out varying only the concentration of reactant A, keeping the concentration of reactant B the same each time.

- The process is repeated, varying the concentration of reactant B and keeping the concentration of reactant A the same each time.

- The rate is determined for each reaction run. This can be done by measuring a suitable property – for example, a change in colour using a colorimeter, the change in pH, volume of gas evolved or changes in mass.

> It is also important to keep the temperature constant during the experiment, or k will change.

> The process is repeated for every reactant involved.

There are various ways of processing the experimental data, once it has been collected.

- Using a **concentration–time graph** (a progress curve). The shape of the graph indicates the order of reaction with respect to the reactant that is changing in concentration.

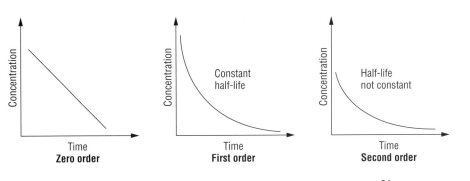

> The half-life ($t_{\frac{1}{2}}$) is the time taken for the concentration of a reactant to halve.

- Using the **half-lives method**. In order to confirm that the reaction is first order, the **half-life** ($t_{\frac{1}{2}}$) can be found.

Several half-lives are determined from the graph and compared. If the half-life is constant, the reaction is first order with respect to that reagent.

- Using a **rate–concentration graph**. This can be drawn by plotting the rate of a reaction against the concentration of a reactant. These results can be obtained from a series of experiments, or by determining the change in rate as a particular reaction progresses. The shape of the graph tells you the order with respect to a particular reactant.

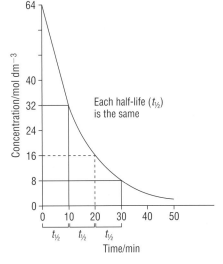

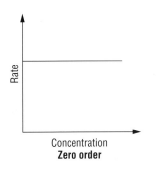

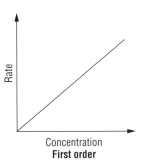

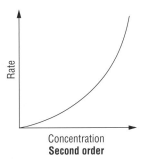

> If a plot of rate against (concentration)^2 gives a straight line, this indicates a second-order reaction.

Reaction mechanisms

An **intermediate** is a chemical formed and then destroyed during the course of a reaction.

A reaction mechanism describes the step-by-step manner in which a chemical reaction occurs.

The slowest step in a multi-step reaction is called the **rate-determining step.** The rate equation for a reaction tells us which particles are involved in the rate-determining step. Consider the following reaction:

By studying rate equations and orders, chemists can deduce a mechanism for a reaction.

$$(CH_3)_3CBr(aq) + OH^-(aq) \rightarrow (CH_3)_3COH(aq) + Br^-(aq) \qquad \textbf{rate} = k[(CH_3)_3CBr]$$

The reaction is first order with respect to 2-bromo-2-methylpropane and zero order with respect to hydroxide ions. This means that the rate-determining step involves only 2-bromo-2-methylpropane.

See page 28 for a summary of reaction kinetics involving enzymes.

$$H_3C - \underset{\underset{CH_3}{|}}{\overset{\overset{CH_3}{|}}{C}} - Br \xrightarrow[\text{(rate-determining step)}]{\text{Step 1}} H_3C - \underset{\underset{CH_3}{|}}{\overset{\overset{CH_3}{|}}{C^+}} \ddot{O}H^- \xrightarrow{\text{Step 2}} H_3C - \underset{\underset{CH_3}{|}}{\overset{\overset{CH_3}{|}}{C}} - OH$$

reactant   carbocation intermediate   product

QUICK CHECK QUESTIONS

1   For each of these reactions, suggest how you could measure the rate:

(a) $2H_2O_2(aq) \xrightarrow{\text{catalase}} 2H_2O(aq) + O_2(g)$
(b) $BrO_3^-(aq) + 5Br^-(aq) + 6H^+(aq) \rightarrow 3Br_2(aq) + 3H_2O(aq)$

2   Use the information given below to write down the order with respect to each reactant, and the overall order for the reaction:
$BrO_3^-(aq) + 5Br^-(aq) + 6H^+(aq) \rightarrow 3Br_2(aq) + 3H_2O(aq)$
rate $= k[BrO_3^-][Br^-][H^+]^2$

3   The reaction between iodide ions and peroxodisulfate ions:
$S_2O_8^{2-}(aq) + 2I^-(aq) \rightarrow 2SO_4^{2-}(aq) + I_2(aq)$
is first order with respect to each reactant. Write the rate equation for the reaction.

4   The table shows data from an experiment to investigate the rate at which an ester is hydrolysed by alkali.

Ester concentration ($\times 10^{-2}\, mol\, dm^{-3}$)	Time (s)
1.00	0
0.68	100
0.48	200
0.30	300
0.22	400
0.12	500

(a) Plot a graph of concentration of ester against time.

(b) Determine two values for the half-life of the reaction.
(c) What is the order of this reaction with respect to the ester?

5   The table shows some data for the reaction between nitrogen(II) oxide and oxygen at 25 °C.

Expt	Initial NO concentration ($mol\, dm^{-3}$)	Initial O_2 concentration ($mol\, dm^{-3}$)	Initial rate ($mol\, dm^{-3}\, s^{-1}$)
1	0.10	0.30	6.0×10^{-5}
2	0.10	0.60	1.2×10^{-4}
3	0.20	0.30	2.4×10^{-4}

Using the data:
(a) find the order of reaction with respect to NO and O_2
(b) find the overall order of the reaction
(c) write the rate equation for the reaction
(d) calculate the value of the rate constant at 25 °C. State the units.

6   The reaction between 1-bromopropane and hydroxide ions takes place in two steps. The rate equation for the reaction is: rate $= k[CH_3CH_2CH_2Br][OH^-]$.
(a) Which species are involved in the rate-determining step of the reaction?
(b) Suggest a mechanism for the reaction.

Optical isomerism

Chemical Ideas 3.5

Stereoisomers are molecules that have the same molecular formula and also have their atoms bonded in the same order, but these atoms are arranged differently in space. There are two types of stereoisomers – **E/Z isomers** (for details refer to page 76 of *Revise AS Chemistry for Salters*) and **optical isomers**.

In order to exhibit optical isomerism, a molecule must have a **chiral centre** – very often, this central atom is carbon, and is called the **chiral carbon** (often shown as *).

CH₃ — Chiral centre
H₂N — C* — COOH
H
alanine

> A chiral centre is an atom that has **four different atoms** or **groups of atoms** attached to it. Molecules with a chiral centre are called **optical isomers** or **enantiomers**.

Molecules with a chiral centre have non-superimposable mirror images.

CH₃   CH₃
HO — C — COOH   HOOC — C — OH
H   H

The two enantiomers of
2-hydroxypropanoic acid (*lactic acid*)

> Exam tip – when drawing optical isomers, emphasise the tetrahedral arrangement of groups around the chiral centre by using wedge and dashed bonds.

Identifying the chiral centre in a molecule containing a carbon ring can be tricky. The carbon ring can behave as two different groups if the two 'halves' of the ring are not symmetrical. Carvone provides a good example of this.

H₃C
   C — * — CH₃
H₂C
          O
carvone

> To draw enantiomers, draw the 3D structure of one enantiomer. Then imagine a mirror is placed next to it and draw the reflection.

There are two ways in which optical isomers behave differently from each other (otherwise, optical isomers have identical chemical reactions and physical properties):

- Optically active molecules rotate the plane of plane-polarised light in different directions. One isomer (called the **laevorotatory**, or L-, isomer) rotates the light clockwise while the other (the **dextrorotatory**, or D-, isomer) rotates the light anticlockwise.

> To indicate a chiral centre, draw an asterisk next to the relevant carbon atom.

- Optical isomers behave differently in the presence of other chiral molecules. For example, the different smells of oranges and lemons are due to the two optical isomers of the molecule limonene interacting with the chiral receptors in your nose.

Some chemical reactions produce a 50:50 mixture of D- and L-optical isomers. This type of mixture is called a **racemic mixture**.

QUICK CHECK QUESTIONS

1 What is a chiral carbon?
2 What are enantiomers (optical isomers)?
3 The amino acid glycine does not exhibit optical isomerism. Why not?
4 Draw the optical isomers of CH₃CH(OH)CN.
5 Identify any chiral centres in the following molecules:
   (a)
   H₃C
      C — ◯ — CH₃
   H₂C

   (b) CH₃CH(NH₂)COOH.

6 Which of the following molecules exhibit optical isomerism?
   (a) butan-2-ol
   (b) 2-chloromethylpropane
   (c) 2,3-dihydroxypropanal
   (d) 3-bromopentane

Amino acids and proteins

Chemical Ideas 13.9

Amino acids are **bifunctional** molecules – they contain both the amino ($-NH_2$) and carboxyl ($-COOH$) functional groups. When these functional groups are attached to the same carbon atom, the amino acid is called an α-amino acid.

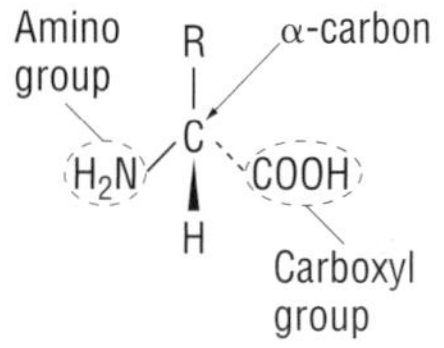

Amino group — R — α-carbon — C — H_2N — COOH — H — Carboxyl group

You do not need to learn the R groups or abbreviations for amino acid names.

All proteins are made from the same set of 20 α-amino acids. The side chain (R) is different in every amino acid. Each amino acid is also known by a three-letter abbreviation – e.g. Ala for alanine, for which $R = CH_3$.

See page 25 for further information on optical isomerism.

Apart from glycine (where $R = H$), α-amino acids have four different groups attached to the α-carbon atom, so they can exhibit **optical isomerism**.

Acid–base reactions

Amino acids can act both as weak acids and as weak bases. The $-COOH$ group donates H^+ ions, while the $-NH_2$ group accepts H^+ ions. Amino acids can exist in three different ionic forms, depending on the pH of the solution they are in. See below:

Watch out for amino acids that have $-NH_2$ or $-COOH$ groups as part of the R group. These will also ionise under acidic or alkaline conditions.

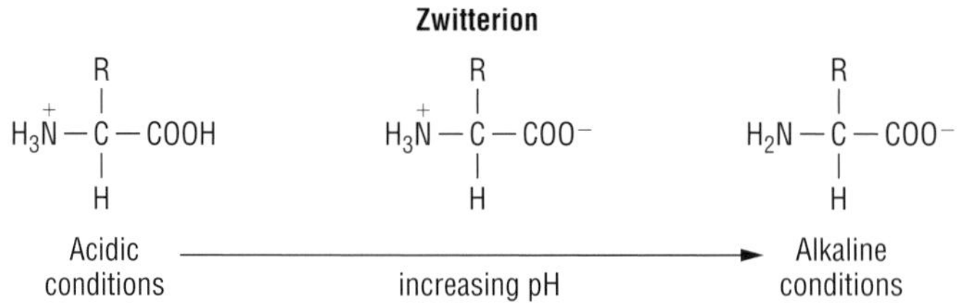

Zwitterion

Acidic conditions — increasing pH — Alkaline conditions

The amino group is protonated in acidic conditions, and the carboxyl group is deprotonated in alkaline conditions. An ion can have both a positive group and a negative group at the same time – these ions are called **zwitterions**.

Forming dipeptides, polypeptides and proteins

When naming a dipeptide, start at the residue with the free NH_2 group.

Two amino acids can join together to form a dipeptide. The $-NH_2$ group from one amino acid reacts with the $-COOH$ group from the second amino acid, forming a **secondary amide group** or **peptide link**.

Water is eliminated, making this a condensation reaction.

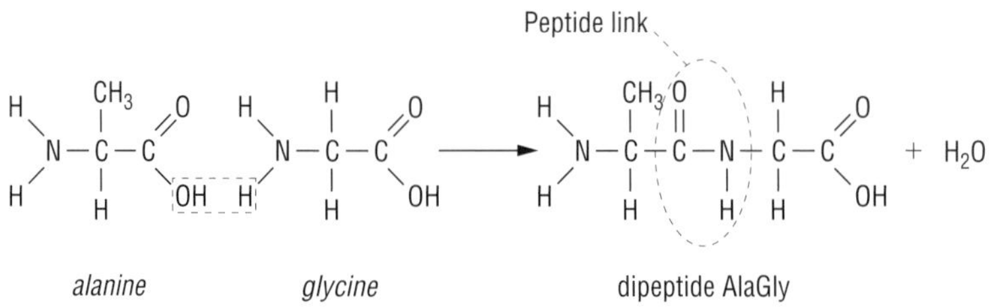

Peptide link

alanine   *glycine*   dipeptide AlaGly

When several amino acids are joined together in this way, a **polypeptide** is formed. **Proteins** are naturally occurring condensation polymers formed when many amino acids join together.

The structure of proteins

The order in which amino acids join together is called the **primary structure** of a protein. When a polypeptide chain forms an alpha **helix** or beta **sheet** this is called its **secondary structure**. Both helix and sheet arrangements occur as a result of hydrogen bonding.

The 'global' folding of a polypeptide chain to give it a unique shape is called its **tertiary structure**. There are four types of interaction responsible for maintaining tertiary structure:

- instantaneous dipole–induced dipole bonds between non-polar side chains
- hydrogen bonds between polar side chains
- ionic bonds between ionisable side chains
- covalent bonds (e.g. 'sulfur bridges').

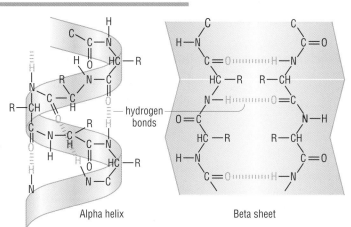

Alpha helix   Beta sheet

> Both an alpha helix and a beta sheet are held in place by hydrogen bonding.

Hydrolysis of peptides/proteins

When a peptide or protein is refluxed with moderately concentrated acid or alkali for several hours, the C—N bond in the peptide link is broken. Under acidic hydrolysis conditions, the $-NH_2$ groups are protonated to give $-NH_3^+$ whereas under alkaline hydrolysis conditions the $-COOH$ deprotonates to give $-COO^-$. For example:

> You can review intermolecular bonding by reading pages 46, 47, 71 and 72 of *Revise AS Chemistry for Salters*.

> Learn the key conditions for hydrolysis – heating with moderately concentrated ($4\,mol\,dm^{-3}$) HCl under reflux.

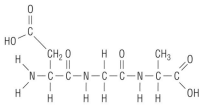

The amino acids produced by peptide hydrolysis can be identified using thin-layer chromatography and the use of ninhydrin as a locating agent (see page vi).

> This is amide hydrolysis – see page 17.

QUICK CHECK QUESTIONS

1   Draw the structure of the amino acid cysteine, where R = CH_2SH.
2   Draw the structures of the products formed when valine ($R = CH(CH_3)_2$) dissolves in:
   (a) an alkaline solution
   (b) a neutral solution
   (c) an acidic solution.
3   Draw the structures of the two different dipeptides that can be produced when glycine (R = H) reacts with serine ($R = CH_2OH$).
4   Explain what the following terms mean, with reference to proteins:
   (a) primary structure
   (b) secondary structure
   (c) tertiary structure.

5   Draw the products of the reaction when the tripeptide:

is hydrolysed using
(a) $1\,mol\,dm^{-3}$ NaOH
(b) $4\,mol\,dm^{-3}$ HCl.

Enzymes and atom economy

Chemical Ideas 10.4 and 15.9

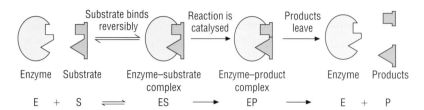

Enzyme   Substrate   Enzyme–substrate   Enzyme–product   Enzyme   Products
                     complex   complex

$$E + S \rightleftharpoons ES \longrightarrow EP \longrightarrow E + P$$

Enzymes are metabolic catalysts that are proteins. They have a high **specificity** for a given substrate. All enzymes have an **active site**, where the tertiary structure of the enzyme exactly matches the structure of its substrate. The substrate can weakly bind to the surface of the active site.

> Enzymes are used in many applications – for example in diabetes test strips, in making cheese and for supplementing washing powders.

This may weaken bonds in the substrate or slightly alter its shape, allowing reaction to occur. After reaction, the products can leave the active site and the process is repeated.

Any changes to the shape of the active site – such as disruption of hydrogen bonds on heating, or disruption of ionic interactions through changes in pH – will result in the enzyme being denatured, and losing its activity.

If a molecule of similar shape to the substrate enters and binds strongly to the active site it might not react but still occupy that site, preventing entry of the correct substrate. This is called **competitive inhibition**.

Enzyme-catalysed reactions

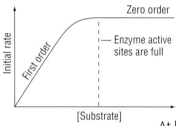

Unusually, enzyme-catalysed reactions have different rate equations at high and at low substrate concentration.

At low concentrations of substrate, the rate equation is rate = k[E][S]. There are plenty of active sites for the substrate to bind to – so doubling the substrate concentration doubles the rate of reaction. The reaction is first order with respect to the substrate.

> See pages 22–24 for details on order of reactions.

At high concentrations of substrate, the rate equation is rate = k[E] because all the active sites on the enzyme molecules have become **saturated**. The reaction becomes zero order with respect to the substrate. A similar shaped graph is generated when enzyme concentration is plotted against initial rate.

Enzymes in industry

Enzymes are used increasingly as catalysts in industry because:
- they are **specific** – they can 'select' a particular substrate from a feedstock containing a mixture of reactants
- they work effectively at low temperatures – this helps reduce the energy costs of an industrial process
- they work well in an aqueous environment – this reduces the need for organic solvents, which can be flammable and damaging to the environment

> See page 7 for details on atom economy.

- they can often convert reactant to product in a one-step reaction – this increases the percentage **atom economy** of the process.

QUICK CHECK QUESTIONS

1   What is meant by the following words when referring to enzymes:
    (a) specificity
    (b) inhibitor?
2   Explain why most enzymes will not catalyse reactions
    (a) at very high or low pH
    (b) at high temperatures.

3   (a) Draw a graph to show how the initial rate of reaction varies with enzyme concentration for an enzyme-catalysed reaction.
    (b) Explain how and why the order of reaction with an enzyme is different at low substrate and high substrate concentrations.
4   Give three advantages of using enzymes to catalyse reactions on an industrial scale.

The Steel Story (SS)

Steel is one of the world's most versatile metals. This module looks at how steel is made and why it rusts. It also takes a detailed look at the properties of iron and other transition metals. 'CI' refers to sections in your *Chemical Ideas* textbook. 'Storylines' refers to your *Chemical Storylines* textbook.

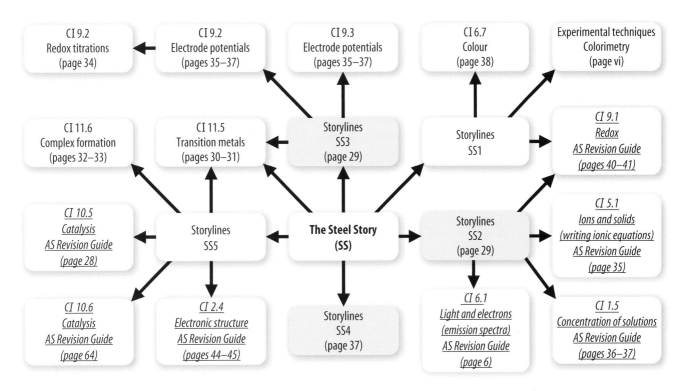

CI 9.2
Redox titrations
(page 34)

CI 9.2
Electrode potentials
(pages 35–37)

CI 9.3
Electrode potentials
(pages 35–37)

CI 6.7
Colour
(page 38)

Experimental techniques
Colorimetry
(page vi)

CI 11.6
Complex formation
(pages 32–33)

CI 11.5
Transition metals
(pages 30–31)

Storylines
SS3
(page 29)

Storylines
SS1

CI 9.1
Redox
AS Revision Guide
(pages 40–41)

CI 10.5
Catalysis
AS Revision Guide
(page 28)

Storylines
SS5

**The Steel Story
(SS)**

Storylines
SS2
(page 29)

CI 5.1
Ions and solids
(writing ionic equations)
AS Revision Guide
(page 35)

CI 10.6
Catalysis
AS Revision Guide
(page 64)

CI 2.4
Electronic structure
AS Revision Guide
(pages 44–45)

Storylines
SS4
(page 37)

CI 6.1
Light and electrons
(emission spectra)
AS Revision Guide
(page 6)

CI 1.5
Concentration of solutions
AS Revision Guide
(pages 36–37)

Note: Italicised and underlined text refers to work *first* met at AS.

Note: Storylines content that relates to learning outcomes (spec. statements) that cannot be found elsewhere is shaded.

From *Chemical Storylines*, you also need to be aware of the following.

Extracting and purifying metals (Storylines SS2)

Most metals are found as compounds in the Earth's crust. Metal ores are mined, and the metal extracted by **reduction**. The method depends on the reactivity of the metal. Reactive metals (Groups 1 and 2 and aluminium) are extracted by **electrolysis**. Less reactive metals (e.g. iron and zinc) are obtained from their ores by **reduction with carbon** or **carbon monoxide**. Unreactive metals (e.g. gold and silver) can be found as elements in the Earth's crust.

Preventing corrosion (Storylines SS3)

- **Barrier protection** – prevents oxygen and/or water coming into contact with iron and steel. Examples include painting, greasing, oiling and using polymer coatings.
- **Galvanising** – steel can be covered in a thin layer of protective zinc that oxidises. Stainless steel contains chromium that oxidises, also leaving a protective oxide layer.
- **Sacrificial protection** – attaching blocks of a more reactive metal (e.g. zinc) to large iron structures such as ships. An electrochemical cell is formed and the reactive metal corrodes preferentially.

The d block: transition metals

Chemical Ideas 11.5

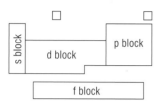

Outline of the Periodic Table

A copy of the Periodic Table is given on the inside front cover and will be given in the *Data Sheet* used in your written examinations.

Electronic arrangements of the d-block elements in Period 4:

Sc	$[Ar]3d^1 4s^2$
Ti	$[Ar]3d^2 4s^2$
V	$[Ar]3d^3 4s^2$
Cr	$[Ar]3d^5 4s^1$
Mn	$[Ar]3d^5 4s^2$
Fe	$[Ar]3d^6 4s^2$
Co	$[Ar]3d^7 4s^2$
Ni	$[Ar]3d^8 4s^2$
Cu	$[Ar]3d^{10} 4s^1$
Zn	$[Ar]3d^{10} 4s^2$
$[Ar] = 1s^2 2s^2 2p^6 3s^2 3p^6$	

The transition metals are found in the d block of the Periodic Table. The d block contains over 30 elements. In each of the first three rows (Periods 4, 5 and 6) there are ten elements. This chapter focuses on the properties of the first row of ten elements, from scandium (Sc) to zinc (Zn).

Electronic arrangements

The properties of the ten elements from scandium to zinc are remarkably similar. This is because each additional electron enters the 3d sub-shell as the atomic number increases. The 4s sub-shell has slightly lower energy than the (inner) 3d sub-shell and is filled first. Note the unusual electron arrangements for Cr and Cu – this is due to the additional stability associated with a half-full and a completely full 3d sub-shell.

A **transition metal** is defined as a d-block element that forms at least one ion with a **partially filled sub-shell** of d electrons.

When d-block elements react to form ions, the 4s electrons are the first to be lost. For example:

$$Fe\,[Ar]3d^6 4s^2 \rightarrow Fe^{2+}\,[Ar]3d^6 4s^0 \rightarrow Fe^{3+}\,[Ar]3d^5 4s^0$$

Scandium and zinc don't display the chemical properties associated with the transition metals because their ions (Sc^{3+} and Zn^{2+}) have electron arrangements $3d^0$ and $3d^{10}$ respectively.

Physical properties

In comparison with the s-block metals, d-block metals are also good conductors of heat and electricity but they are denser and have higher melting and boiling points. They are hard and durable, with high tensile strength and good mechanical properties. This makes them ideal for a wide range of uses, both as pure metals and in alloys.

Chemical properties

The transition metals have four important chemical properties, all of which relate directly to the electronic arrangements of the elements or their ions. These are:

- variable oxidation states
- formation of coloured ions
- formation of complexes
- catalytic activity.

Manganese has three common oxidation states:

+2, e.g. in Mn^{2+}

+4, e.g. in MnO_2

+7, e.g. in MnO_4^-

Variable oxidation states

This happens because the differences between successive ionisation enthalpies in the 3d and 4s sub-shells are relatively small, so multiple electron loss is possible.

In the lower oxidation states, the elements exist as simple ions (e.g. Cu^{2+}, Cr^{3+}, Fe^{2+}, Fe^{3+}), but in the higher oxidation states they are covalently bonded to electronegative elements, such as oxygen or fluorine, forming anions (e.g. $Cr_2O_7^{2-}$, MnO_4^-, VO_3^-).

Redox reactions are a key feature of transition metal chemistry. Compounds containing transition metals in high oxidation states tend to be oxidising agents, whereas compounds with transition metals in low oxidation states are often reducing agents.

You can find out about naming these ions by looking at page 40 in *Revise AS Chemistry for Salters*.

You should recall from AS Chemistry that oxidation can be defined as the loss of electrons or an increase in oxidation number. Reduction is the gain of electrons or a decrease in oxidation number. For example:

$$MnO_4^-(aq) + 8H^+(aq) + 5Fe^{2+}(aq) \rightarrow Mn^{2+}(aq) + 4H_2O(l) + 5Fe^{3+}(aq)$$

This reaction between manganate(VII) ions and iron(II) ions can be written as two half-equations:

$$MnO_4^-(aq) + 8H^+(aq) + 5e^- \rightarrow Mn^{2+}(aq)$$

in which manganate(VII) ions have gained electrons. The oxidation state of manganese has gone from +7 down to +2. This is reduction.

$$5Fe^{2+}(aq) \rightarrow 5Fe^{3+}(aq) + 5e^-$$

in which iron(II) ions have lost electrons. The oxidation state of iron has gone from +2 up to +3. This is oxidation.

> Redox reactions can be reviewed in *Revise AS Chemistry for Salters* on pages 40 and 41.

Formation of coloured ions

Transition metal compounds show many different colours. Electron transitions occur within the 3d sub-shell when visible light is absorbed – this can only happen in ions that have a partially filled 3d sub-shell. A fuller explanation of why transition metal ions appear coloured is given on page 61.

> Common colours associated with ions:
> $Cu^{2+}(aq)$ blue
> $Fe^{2+}(aq)$ green
> $Fe^{3+}(aq)$ yellow/orange.

Formation of complexes

Transition metals are able to form complexes because their 3d orbitals can accommodate the electrons donated by the ligands. For further details about complexes see pages 32–33.

Catalytic activity

Many catalysts are made from transition metals or their compounds. The metals can act as **heterogeneous** catalysts, providing a surface onto which gaseous reactant molecules are adsorbed. Weak interactions between these and the 3d and 4s electrons of the transition metal keep the molecules in place while bonds are broken and formed.

Transition metal ions can also act as **homogeneous** catalysts. This is because they are able to change from one oxidation state to another during the reaction, before returning to their original oxidation state. For example, Fe^{2+} ions catalyse the oxidation of iodide ions by peroxodisulfate ions.

> Some important heterogeneous catalysts are Fe used in the Haber process, V_2O_5 used in the contact process, Ni used in hydrogenation, and Pt/Rh used in catalytic converters.

QUICK CHECK QUESTIONS

1 Write the electron arrangements of the following transition metal ions:
 (a) Ti^{2+}
 (b) Cr^{3+}
 (c) V^{3+}.

2 Give the oxidation state of the transition metal in each of the following:
 (a) CrO_4^{2-}
 (b) MnO_2
 (c) VO_2^+.

3 Copper can form Cu^+ and Cu^{2+} ions. Is copper a transition metal?

4 A solution of sodium potassium tartrate is oxidised by hydrogen peroxide solution to carbon dioxide, water and methanoate ions. The reaction is catalysed by $Co^{2+}(aq)$ ions.
 (a) Is this an example of heterogeneous catalysis or homogeneous catalysis? Explain your answer.
 (b) Suggest what happens to the Co^{2+} ions during the course of the reaction.

5 What are the most common oxidation states of iron? What are their colours?

6 Show that the reaction below is a redox reaction by writing it as two half-equations:
 $$Cr_2O_7^{2-}(aq) + 3SO_2(aq) + 2H^+(aq) \rightarrow$$
 $$3SO_4^{2-}(aq) + 2Cr^{3+}(aq) + H_2O(l)$$

Complex formation

Chemical Ideas 11.6

lone pair of electrons
on oxygen forms
the dative bond

$$\left[\begin{array}{c} OH_2 \\ H_2O \cdots \overset{\displaystyle OH_2}{\underset{\displaystyle H_2O}{\text{Cu}}} \cdots OH_2 \\ H_2O \end{array}\right]^{2+}$$

dative covalent bonds

ligand

In a complex, a central metal atom or ion is surrounded by ligands. Ligands are molecules or anions with one or more lone pairs of electrons. An example of a complex ion is $[Cu(H_2O)_6]^{2+}$, shown on the left.

Ligands form **dative covalent bonds** with the central metal atom or ion. The number of bonds between the central metal and the ligands is called the **coordination number** of the central metal. The complex copper(II) ion shown on the left has a coordination number of 6.

Shapes of complexes

> If a complex has an overall charge, it is called a **complex ion**. Always draw a square bracket round a complex ion and write the charge outside the bracket.

Complexes with coordination number 6 are generally **octahedral** in shape. Those with coordination number 4 are usually **tetrahedral** but can be **square planar**, while those with coordination number 2 are **linear**.

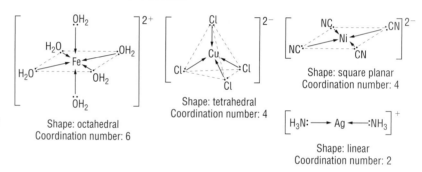

Shape: octahedral
Coordination number: 6

Shape: tetrahedral
Coordination number: 4

Shape: square planar
Coordination number: 4

Shape: linear
Coordination number: 2

> A single edta^{4-} ion can form a hexadentate complex by wrapping itself around the central transition metal ion. This is known as **chelation**.

Types of ligands

Ligands can form **one** bond to the central metal (**monodentate**), **two** bonds (**bidentate**) or **many** bonds (**polydentate**). Here are the names and formulae of some common ligands:

Molecule/ion	Formula	Name of ligand	Type of ligand
water	H_2O	aqua	monodentate
ammonia	NH_3	ammine	monodentate
chloride ion	Cl^-	chloro	monodentate
cyanide ion	CN^-	cyano	monodentate
hydroxide ion	OH^-	hydroxo	monodentate
ethanedioate ion	$(COO^-)_2$	ethanedioate	bidentate
ethylenediaminetetracetate ion	edta^{4-} (you don't need to remember the full formula!)	edta	polydentate

Naming complexes

The name of a complex can be worked out by applying the following rules, in order:

- Write the number of each type of ligand, using the prefixes mono-, di-, tri-, tetra-, penta-, hexa-.
- Write the name of each ligand (in alphabetical order).

- Write the name of the central metal – use the English name if the overall charge on the complex is positive or neutral, and the Latinised name if it is negative.
- Write the oxidation number of the central metal, in brackets.

For example:

- $[CuCl_4]^{2-}$ is called the tetrachlorocuprate(II) ion
- $[Cu(NH_3)_4(H_2O)_2]^{2+}$ is called the tetraamminediaquacopper(II) ion.

Metal	Latinised name
Cu	cuprate
V	vanadate
Ti	titanate
Ag	argentate
Zn	zincate
Pb	plumbate
Cr	chromate

Colour in complexes

When light falls on a complex, some frequencies are absorbed and some are reflected or transmitted. If *visible* light is absorbed, the complex will appear coloured. The presence of ligands causes the five d orbitals of the central metal to 'split' – some orbitals become slightly higher in energy and some slightly lower in energy. The small energy gap between these orbitals allows visible light to be absorbed. The colour of the complex (the colour we see) is the complementary colour to that absorbed.

You can find out more about colour in complexes on page 61.

Ligand substitution reactions

These are reactions in which one ligand displaces another. For example, if concentrated hydrochloric acid is added to a solution of copper(II) sulfate(VI), chloride ligands replace water ligands, and the solution changes colour from blue to yellow. Ligand substitution occurs if the new complex formed is more stable than the previous complex.

Ligand substitution reactions are also called ligand exchange reactions.

$$[Cu(H_2O)_6]^{2+} + 4Cl^-(aq) \rightarrow [CuCl_4]^{2-}(aq) + 6H_2O(aq)$$
　　blue　　　　　　　　　　　　yellow

Precipitation reactions of $Cu^{2+}(aq)$, $Fe^{2+}(aq)$ and $Fe^{3+}(aq)$

Solutions containing copper(II), iron(II) or iron(III) ions form coloured precipitates with sodium hydroxide solution:

Be sure you can write the ionic equations for each of these reactions.

$$Fe^{2+}(aq) + 2OH^-(aq) \rightarrow Fe(OH)_2(s) \text{ – green gelatinous solid}$$

$$Fe^{3+}(aq) + 3OH^-(aq) \rightarrow Fe(OH)_3(s) \text{ – orange gelatinous solid}$$

$$Cu^{2+}(aq) + 2OH^-(aq) \rightarrow Cu(OH)_2(s) \text{ – pale blue solid}$$

If ammonia solution is added to a solution containing copper(II) ions, a dark blue/violet solution forms:

The same dark blue/violet solution forms if ammonia solution is added to $Cu(OH)_2(s)$. This is an example of ligand substitution.

$$[Cu(H_2O)_6]^{2+}(aq) + 4NH_3(aq) \rightarrow [Cu(NH_3)_4(H_2O)_2]^{2+}(aq) + 4H_2O(l)$$

The larger the value of its stability constant, K_{stab}, the more stable a complex is.

QUICK CHECK QUESTIONS

1 Explain what is meant by the following terms:
   (a) ligand
   (b) complex ion
   (c) coordination number
   (d) dative covalent bond.
2 Name and draw the shapes of the following complexes:
   (a) $[Cr(H_2O)_6]^{3+}$
   (b) $[CoCl_4]^{2-}$
   (c) $[Fe(OH)_2(H_2O)_4]^+$
3 Explain why the complex ion $[CuCl_4]^{2-}$ is yellow in colour.

4 Use the equation below to help you to answer these questions:
   $$[Cu(H_2O)_6]^{2+}(aq) + 4NH_3(aq) \rightarrow$$
   $$[Cu(NH_3)_4(H_2O)_2]^{2+}(aq) + 4H_2O(l)$$
   (a) What colour is the complex ion $[Cu(H_2O)_6]^{2+}(aq)$?
   (b) What colour is the complex ion $[Cu(NH_3)_4(H_2O)_2]^{2+}$?
   (c) What *type* of reaction is taking place?
   (d) Which of the two complex ions is more stable?
5 Write ionic equations for the reaction of sodium hydroxide with:
   (a) copper(II) ions
   (b) iron(III) ions in aqueous solution.

Redox and redox titrations

Chemical Ideas 9.2

All redox reactions involve electron transfer. Remember:

OILRIG – **Oxidation is loss** of electrons. **Reduction is gain** of electrons.

A reducing agent **donates electrons** while an oxidising agent **accepts electrons**.

You can find out how to assign oxidation states on pages 40–41 of *Revise AS Chemistry for Salters*.

See page vi of *Revise AS Chemistry for Salters* for details of acid–base titrations

The manganate(VII) ion is acidified with sulfuric acid and not hydrochloric acid because it would oxidise the chloride ions in the latter.

1 mole of MnO_4^- reacts with 5 moles of Fe^{2+}.

For calculations involving titrations, see page 36 of *Revise AS Chemistry for Salters*.

Activity ES4.1 uses an iodine–thiosulfate titration to estimate the concentration of bleach solutions.

You have already studied acid–base titrations in AS Chemistry. The practical techniques involved in redox titrations are similar – the key difference is that the type of reaction involved is a redox reaction. In both acid–base and redox titrations, a solution of known concentration is reacted with a solution of unknown concentration, and the unknown concentration is found by calculation.

Potassium manganate(VII) titrations

Potassium manganate(VII) solution is a strong oxidising agent and can be used in redox titrations to find the concentration of solutions containing iron(II) ions or hydrogen peroxide. No indicator is required because the distinctive purple colour of potassium manganate(VII) disappears as it reacts.

A typical procedure is to:

- use a pipette to transfer a known volume of the test solution (containing Fe^{2+} ions, for example) into a conical flask
- acidify this solution with dilute sulfuric acid
- slowly add potassium manganate(VII) to the solution in the conical flask from a burette, swirling gently, until a pale pink colour persists
- repeat the titration until you have two titres within $0.1\,cm^3$.

During the titration, iron(II) ions are oxidised to iron(III) ions, and manganate(VII) ions are reduced to manganese(II) ions. The ionic equation for the reaction is:

$$5Fe^{2+}(aq) + MnO_4^-(aq) + 8H^+(aq) \rightarrow 5Fe^{3+}(aq) + Mn^{2+}(aq) + 4H_2O(l)$$

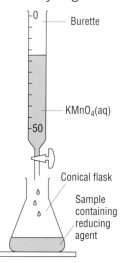

Burette

$KMnO_4(aq)$

Conical flask

Sample containing reducing agent

Iodine–thiosulfate titrations

These titrations are often used to find the concentration of solutions of oxidising agents. A known amount of the oxidising agent reacts with an excess of acidified potassium iodide solution. The iodine produced is then titrated against a standard solution of sodium thiosulfate. Near the end-point of the reaction, a few drops of starch solution are added, giving an intense blue/black colour – this disappears at the end-point. The equation for the reaction is:

$$2S_2O_3^{2-}(aq) + I_2(aq) \rightarrow S_4O_6^{2-}(aq) + 2I^-(aq)$$

QUICK CHECK QUESTIONS

1 Name two chemicals whose concentration could be determined by redox titration with potassium manganate(VII).

2 A solution of potassium manganate(VII) (in a burette) is titrated with a solution of iron(II) ions (in a conical flask).
   (a) What colour change is observed in the conical flask?
   (b) How is the end-point of the reaction determined?

3 What is the change in oxidation state of manganese during the reaction described in question **2**?

4 $22.4\,cm^3$ of $0.0200\,mol\,dm^{-3}$ $KMnO_4$ solution reacted with exactly $25.0\,cm^3$ of a solution containing $Fe^{2+}(aq)$ ions.

   (a) Calculate the number of moles of $KMnO_4$ used in the titration.
   (b) Calculate the concentration of the solution of $Fe^{2+}(aq)$ ions.

5 Manganate(VII) ions react with ethanedioic acid ions in a redox reaction. The half-equation for the oxidation of ethanedioic acid is $(COOH)_2 \rightarrow 2CO_2(g) + 2H^+(aq) + 2e^-$. Using the half-equation for the reduction of $MnO_4^-(aq)$ ions met earlier, construct the overall equation for the reaction.

6 Describe how the concentration of a solution of bleach can be determined using an iodine–thiosulfate titration.

Electrode potentials

Chemical Ideas 9.2 and 9.3

Redox reactions

Redox reactions can be considered to be two different reactions occurring simultaneously. One is a reduction, and the other an oxidation. The equation for each is called a half-equation and involves ions and electrons.

Combining half-equations

Adding together the two half-equations gives the overall equation for the redox reaction.

STEP 1 Write the half-equations for the oxidation and reduction reactions:

$SO_3^{2-}(aq) + H_2O(l) \rightarrow SO_4^{2-}(aq) + 2H^+(aq) + 2e^-$ **oxidation** half-reaction

$Cr_2O_7^{2-}(aq) + 14H^+(aq) + 6e^- \rightarrow 2Cr^{3+}(aq) + 7H_2O(l)$ **reduction** half-reaction

STEP 2 Make the number of electrons the same in each half-equation:

$\mathbf{3}SO_3^{2-}(aq) + \mathbf{3}H_2O(l) \rightarrow \mathbf{3}SO_4^{2-}(aq) + \mathbf{6}H^+(aq) + \mathbf{6}e^-$

$Cr_2O_7^{2-}(aq) + 14H^+(aq) + \mathbf{6}e^- \rightarrow 2Cr^{3+}(aq) + 7H_2O(l)$

STEP 3 Add the two half-equations together:

$Cr_2O_7^{2-}(aq) + 8H^+(aq) + 3SO_3^{2-}(aq) \rightarrow 2Cr^{3+}(aq) + 4H_2O(l) + 3SO_4^{2-}(aq)$

> Electrode potentials (see later) allow you to decide which is the oxidation half-reaction and which is the reduction half-reaction.

> No electrons appear in the final ionic equation, because they cancel out.

Electrode potentials

When a metal is placed in an aqueous solution of its ions, an **equilibrium** is established. A potential difference, or **electrode potential**, is created between the metal and the solution of ions. For example:

$Cu^{2+}(aq) + 2e^- \rightleftharpoons Cu(s)$ $Fe^{2+}(aq) + 2e^- \rightleftharpoons Fe(s)$

The greater the tendency of a metal to release electrons and form ions, the more negative is its electrode potential. Altering the temperature or the concentration of ions in solution alters the value of the electrode potential.

Electrochemical cells

It is not possible to measure the electrode potential of a single half-cell. Two half-cells must be connected together to make an **electrochemical cell**. The potential difference between the two half-cells is called the cell potential or e.m.f., E_{cell}.

When two half-cells are joined:

- the one with the more negative electrode potential becomes the negative terminal of the electrochemical cell
- the one with the more positive electrode potential becomes the positive terminal
- electrons flow in the external circuit from the negative terminal to the positive terminal.

> Notice in the diagram that the Fe^{2+}/Fe redox couple has a more negative electrode potential than the Cu^{2+}/Cu redox couple. Notice that the oxidised species is always written first.

> A **salt bridge** provides an ionic connection between two half-cells. It is usually made from a strip of filter paper soaked in a saturated solution of potassium nitrate.
>
> A high-resistance voltmeter measures the maximum potential difference between two half-cells – the cell potential, E_{cell}.

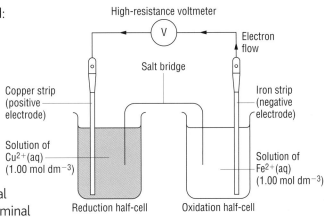

High-resistance voltmeter

Electron flow

Salt bridge

Copper strip (positive electrode)

Iron strip (negative electrode)

Solution of $Cu^{2+}(aq)$ (1.00 mol dm^{-3})

Solution of $Fe^{2+}(aq)$ (1.00 mol dm^{-3})

Reduction half-cell   Oxidation half-cell

Standard electrode potentials

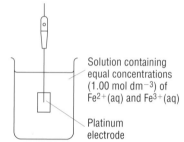

H$_2$(g) at 298 K and 1 atm

Glass tube with holes in to allow bubbles of H$_2$(g) to escape

Platinum electrode

Acid solution containing 1 mol dm^{-3} H$^+$(aq)

The **standard hydrogen half-cell** (shown on the left) is chosen as the reference electrode against which all other electrode potentials are measured. Its electrode potential under **standard conditions** is defined as 0.00 V.

The half-reaction occurring in the standard hydrogen half-cell is:

$$H^+(aq) + e^- \rightarrow \tfrac{1}{2}H_2(g)$$

The **standard electrode potential**, $E^{\ominus}$, of a half-cell is defined as the potential difference between it and a standard hydrogen half-cell. By convention, the half-reactions are always written as reduction processes (i.e. with the oxidised species and electrons on the left-hand side).

> Standard conditions are:
>
> Temperature   298 K
> Pressure   1 atm
> Concentration
> 1.00 mol dm^{-3} (all ions).

To measure a standard electrode potential, the half-cell being investigated is connected to a standard hydrogen half-cell. For half-cells involving molecules and ions (I$_2$/2I$^-$) or ions (Fe^{3+}/Fe^{2+}), an inert electrode such as platinum is dipped into a solution containing all the ions and molecules involved in the half-reaction. An Fe^{3+}/Fe^{2+} half-cell is shown on the right.

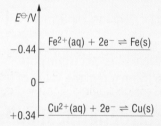

Solution containing equal concentrations (1.00 mol dm^{-3}) of Fe^{2+}(aq) and Fe^{3+}(aq)

Platinum electrode

WORKED EXAMPLE

Finding $E^{\ominus}_{cell}$

For example, what is $E^{\ominus}_{cell}$ when the Fe^{2+}/Fe and Cu^{2+}/Cu half-cells are connected?

STEP 1 Look up the standard electrode potentials for the two half-reactions:

$$Fe^{2+}(aq) + 2e^- \rightarrow Fe(s) \qquad E^{\ominus} = -0.44\,V$$
$$Cu^{2+}(aq) + 2e^- \rightarrow Cu(s) \qquad E^{\ominus} = +0.34\,V$$

> Both half-cells might have negative $E^{\ominus}$ values. In this case, the one with the least negative value has the most positive $E^{\ominus}$.

STEP 2 Construct an electrode potential chart (see right). The half-cell with the most positive electrode potential is at the bottom of the chart.

$E^{\ominus}$/V

-0.44 Fe^{2+}(aq) + 2e$^-$ ⇌ Fe(s)

0

$+0.34$ Cu^{2+}(aq) + 2e$^-$ ⇌ Cu(s)

STEP 3 Find the difference between the two $E^{\ominus}$ values, i.e. $E^{\ominus}_{cell} = +0.78\,V$.

Alternatively, $E^{\ominus}_{cell} = E^{\ominus}$[most positive electrode] $- E^{\ominus}$[most negative electrode]

$$E_{cell} = +0.34\,V - (-0.44\,V) = +0.78\,V$$

> E_{cell} values are always positive.

Predicting the direction of a reaction

The key idea to remember is that the half-cell with the more negative electrode potential supplies electrons to the half-cell with the more positive electrode potential.

To predict the feasibility of the reaction between aqueous chlorine and potassium iodide solution, we calculate $E^{\ominus}_{cell}$.

STEP 1 Look up the half-reactions and their standard electrode potentials:

$$I_2(aq) + 2e^- \rightarrow 2I^-(aq) \qquad E^{\ominus} = +0.54\,V \qquad \text{half-reaction 1}$$
$$Cl_2(g) + 2e^- \rightarrow 2Cl^-(aq) \qquad E^{\ominus} = +1.36\,V \qquad \text{half-reaction 2}$$

STEP 2 Identify which half reaction has the more negative electrode potential. Rewrite that reaction to show it **supplying** electrons (i.e. with the electrons on the right-hand side). Half-reaction 1 has the more negative $E^{\ominus}$, so this half-reaction is rewritten:

$$2I^-(aq) \rightarrow I_2(aq) + 2e^-$$

STEP 3 Balance the number of electrons, and then add the half-reactions:

$$2I^-(aq) + Cl_2(g) \rightarrow I_2(aq) + 2Cl^-(aq) \text{ (the electrons balance as written)}$$

$$E^{\ominus}_{\text{cell}} = E^{\ominus}[\text{positive electrode}] - E^{\ominus}[\text{negative electrode}]$$

$$= +1.36V - (+0.54V) = +0.82V$$

Rusting

Rusting is an electrochemical process. The two half-reactions involved in the initial stage are:

$$Fe^{2+}(aq) + 2e^- \rightarrow Fe(s) \qquad\qquad E^{\ominus} = -0.44V$$

$$O_2(g) + 2H_2O(l) + 4e^- \rightarrow 4OH^-(aq) \quad E^{\ominus} = +0.40V$$

Rust forms in a series of secondary reactions:

(i) $Fe^{2+}(aq) + 2OH^-(aq) \rightarrow Fe(OH)_2(s)$

(ii) $Fe(OH)_2(s) \xrightarrow{\quad O_2(aq)\quad} Fe_2O_3 \cdot xH_2O(s)$

Half-cell	$E^{\ominus}$(V)
$Zn^{2+}(aq)/Zn(s)$	−0.76
$Fe^{3+}(aq)/Fe^{2+}(aq)$	+0.77
$Cu^{2+}(aq)/Cu(s)$	+0.34
$Ag^+(aq)/Ag(s)$	+0.80

> This method can be used to predict the feasibility of a reaction occurring under standard conditions. Even if a reaction turns out to be feasible, it may still not happen because its activation enthalpy is high. A catalyst might enable the reaction to occur. Changing the conditions such as concentration and/or temperature will change the $E^{\ominus}$ values, which may also cause the reaction to happen.

> At the edges of a water droplet, oxygen concentrations are higher, and oxygen is reduced to hydroxide ions. Away from the edges, iron atoms are oxidised to iron(II) ions.

Why recycle steel? (Storylines SS4)

Recycling steel saves resources and energy, and helps to reduce waste. Steel is magnetic, so it can easily be separated from other waste. Except for aerosols, all steel used for packaging is easily recycled. Scrap steel is important in the BOS process – it is added to the converter *before* the molten iron is poured in to help reduce 'thermal shock'.

QUICK CHECK QUESTIONS

1 Combine the following half-equations to produce balanced ionic equations:
   (a) $MnO_4^-(aq) + 8H^+(aq) + 5e^- \rightarrow Mn^{2+}(aq) + 4H_2O(l)$
       with $2Cl^-(aq) \rightarrow Cl_2(g) + 2e^-$
   (b) $H_2O_2(aq) + 2H^+(aq) + 2e^- \rightarrow 2H_2O(l)$ with
       $2I^-(aq) \rightarrow I_2(aq) + 2e^-$

2 Describe how you would measure experimentally the standard electrode potential for:
   (a) a Cu^{2+}/Cu half-cell
   (b) a $Cl_2/2Cl^-$ half-cell.

3 Calculate $E^{\ominus}_{\text{cell}}$ for the electrochemical cells made by combining:
   (a) Zn^{2+}/Zn and Fe^{3+}/Fe^{2+}
   (b) Cu^{2+}/Cu and Ag^+/Ag

4 Use the data below to predict if a reaction will occur between the following pairs of chemicals:
   (a) $Fe^{2+}(aq)$ and $Br^-(aq)$
   (b) $Fe^{2+}(aq)$ and $Cr_2O_7^{2-}(aq)$
   (c) $Br^-(aq)$ and $Cr_2O_7^{2-}(aq)$
       $Cr_2O_7^{2-}(aq) + 14H^+(aq) + 6e^- \rightarrow$
          $2Cr^{3+}(aq) + 7H_2O(l)$ $\quad E^{\ominus} = +1.36V$
       $Br_2(aq) + 2e^- \rightarrow 2Br^-(aq)$ $\quad E^{\ominus} = +1.07V$
       $Fe^{3+}(aq) + e^- \rightarrow Fe^{2+}(aq)$ $\quad E^{\ominus} = +0.77V$

5 Write equations for the reactions which occur when iron rusts.

Where does colour come from?

Chemical Ideas 6.7

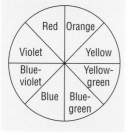
Why does an object appear coloured?

If visible light falls on a coloured object, some wavelengths are absorbed and some are reflected or transmitted. What we see are the reflected or transmitted wavelengths. For example, copper(II) sulfate(VI) solution appears blue because it transmits blue light and absorbs all colours other than blue.

A **colour wheel** can help you to work out which colour(s) are most easily absorbed by an object. A blue object absorbs most strongly in the orange region of the visible spectrum. Orange is called the **complementary colour** to blue – and is opposite blue in the colour wheel. It is the complementary colour that is seen.

Electronic transitions

When visible light falls on a coloured substance, the absorbed light is in the energy range that causes **electronic transitions** – electrons move to higher energy levels and the molecules becomes **excited** (sometimes denoted as * – see below). Molecules do not remain excited for long – as electrons fall back to intermediate energy levels, the energy is re-emitted in various forms, including vibrational energy. There are many different vibrational energy levels within each electronic energy level.

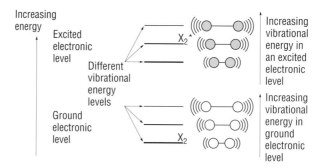

Colorimetry

Colorimetry is an experimental technique used to find the concentration of a coloured solution. The amount of light absorbed by a solution – its **absorbance** – is proportional to the concentration of the solution.

QUICK CHECK QUESTIONS

1. What colour light would be most strongly absorbed by:
   (a) a solution of Co^{2+}(aq), which is pink
   (b) a solution of Fe^{3+}(aq), which is yellow?
2. (a) What do we mean by the term 'complementary colour'?
   (b) What is the complementary colour of violet?
3. What happens to the electrons in a molecule when it absorbs visible light?

Synoptic content – using ideas from AS

UNIT F334

The table lists the synoptic content which can be examined in F334 examination papers – in addition to that given on pages 1–38. If you have forgotten these ideas, or you found them difficult at AS, you should revise them before tackling the practice exam-style questions on the following pages. These ideas will have been revisited in the A2 teaching modules WM, DP, TL and/or SS.

Area of study	Details	Revise AS Chemistry for Salters (page)	Chemical Ideas (section)
Types of bonding	Ionic, covalent, dative covalent and metallic	8–9	3.1
Representing atoms, ions and molecules in diagrams	Dot–cross diagrams, metallic bonding	8–9	3.1
	Shapes of simple molecules (3D representation)	10	3.2
	Structural and skeletal formulae	25	12.1
Properties of ionic and covalent compounds	Melting point, solubility in water, conduction of electricity	8–9, 34	3.1, 5.1
	Detail of giant networks	55	5.2
Ions and formulae	Formulae of ionic compounds, oxyanions	12	3.1
	Formulae of oxyanions	40–41	9.1
Electronegativity	Electronegativity, bond polarity and polar molecules	46–47	3.1, 5.3
Intermolecular bonds	Instantaneous dipole–induced dipole, permanent dipole–permanent dipole	46–47	5.3
	Hydrogen bonds	70	5.4
Electronic configuration	Shells	7	2.3
	Sub-shells and orbitals	44	2.4
Redox	Oxidation states, half-equations and ionic equations	40–41	9.1
Recognise and name; write formulae	Alkanes	24–25	12.1
	Alkenes	25	12.2
	Alcohols	23	13.2
	Ethers	23	13.2
	Halogenoalkanes	48–49	13.1
	Aldehydes, ketones	72–73	13.2, 13.7
Reactions of homologous series	Alkenes	66–67	12.2
	Halogenoalkanes	48–49	13.1
	Alcohols	72–73	13.2
Experimental techniques	Distillation	vii	Appendix 1
	Reflux	vii	
	Acid–base titrations	vi	
Isomerism	Structural isomerism	26	3.3
	E/Z isomerism	76	3.4
Writing balanced equations	Balancing equations	12	1.2
	Writing ionic equations	35	5.1
Mole calculations	Balanced chemical equations	17	1.3
	Masses of reagents	17	1.3
	Molecular formulae	2	1.1
	Percentage yield	52	15.7
	Atom economy	52	15.7
	Concentrations of solutions	36–37	1.5
	Volumes of gases	18	1.4
Instrumental techniques	Mass spectrometry	14	6.5

Unit F334
Practice exam-style questions

Note: Each of these practice questions covers a single teaching module (e.g. **What's in a Medicine?**). In your actual exams, each question may cover more than one teaching module.

What's in a Medicine? (WM)

1   The bark and leaves of willow trees were once used as treatments for fevers and for pain relief. Willow bark contains the compound salicin. In the body, salicin is converted by hydrolysis and oxidation into the active chemical, salicylic acid.

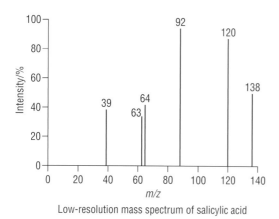

salicin   *salicylic acid*

(a) Name the *type* of alcohol group present in salicin. Explain your answer. [2]
(b) In the laboratory, salicin can be converted into salicylic acid by hydrolysis with dilute sulfuric acid and then oxidation with acidified potassium manganate(VII).
   (i) Name **another** reagent that could be used to oxidise the alcohol group in salicin. [2]
   (ii) Describe a simple test tube reaction that would indicate the presence of the carboxylic acid group in a sample of salicylic acid. [2]
(c) A sample of willow bark is heated under reflux with acidified potassium manganate(VII) solution. A student then analyses the resulting mixture by thin-layer chromatography.
   (i) Suggest why it is necessary for the reaction mixture to be *heated under reflux*. [1]
   (ii) Describe how the thin-layer chromatography would be carried out, and explain how the resulting chromatogram would be used to show that the mixture contains both salicin and salicylic acid. Use labelled diagrams in your answer. [6]

> Ensure you describe the main steps in the practical procedure.

(d) Although effective as a treatment for fevers, salicylic acid can cause some nasty side effects. Chemists modify the structure of salicylic acid by reacting it with ethanoyl chloride, CH_3COCl, to produce aspirin, which is more pleasant to use.
   (i) Draw out the **full structural** formula of ethanoyl chloride. [2]
   (ii) Copy and complete the diagram below to show the **full structural** formula of aspirin. [2]

(e) Spectroscopic methods can be used to investigate the structures of new compounds. The low-resolution mass spectrum of salicylic acid is shown on the left.
   (i) Which peak in the spectrum is the molecular ion peak? [1]
   (ii) What information is provided by the molecular ion peak? [1]
   (iii) Suggest the **molecular formula** of the species responsible for the peak at mass : charge ratio of 120. [2]

Low-resolution mass spectrum of salicylic acid

[Total: 21]

The Materials Revolution (MR)

2 Since the 1980s, threads made from special polyesters have been used to stitch wounds in surgical procedures. The threads disappear as the wound heals. One of the polyesters used is poly(lactic acid).

(a) The repeating unit of poly(lactic acid) is shown below.

$$\left[O - \underset{\underset{\displaystyle H}{|}}{\overset{\overset{\displaystyle CH_3}{|}}{C}} - \overset{\overset{\displaystyle O}{\|}}{C} \right]$$

(i) Draw the structure of the monomer which is used to make poly(lactic acid). [2]

(ii) Explain why the process used to make poly(lactic acid) is called *condensation polymerisation*. [2]

(b) Although the polymer threads are strong, water in the body slowly breaks down the polyester.

(i) Which bond in poly(lactic acid) is broken as the surgical threads are absorbed in the body? [2]

(ii) What *type* of reaction is occurring to cause the threads to break down? [1]

(iii) Suggest why the use of poly(lactic acid) as surgical thread causes no harm to patients. [2]

> What would be the products from the breakdown of the polymer?

(c) Threads used for stitching the fabrics used to make clothes are often polyamides, such as nylon-6,6. Nylon threads are strong and flexible and do not easily break down in water.

$$\left[\overset{\overset{\displaystyle O}{\|}}{C} - (CH_2)_4 - \overset{\overset{\displaystyle O}{\|}}{C} - \underset{\underset{\displaystyle H}{|}}{N} - (CH_2)_6 - \underset{\underset{\displaystyle H}{|}}{N} \right]$$

nylon-6,6

(i) Name the diamine monomer used to make nylon-6,6. [2]

(ii) Explain why nylon fibres are flexible. [1]

(iii) Nylon-6,6 has a higher tensile strength than poly(lactic acid). Explain why, in terms of intermolecular bonds.

QWC: In your answer, you should use appropriate technical terms, spelled correctly. [5]

> Make sure you describe *and* compare the intermolecular bonds in both polymers.

(d) A sample of nylon-6,6 is heated under reflux for several hours with moderately concentrated hydrochloric acid. After cooling, a white solid, hexanedioic acid, is observed in the reaction flask.

Describe how you would obtain a sample of pure hexanedioic acid from the reaction mixture. [5]

(e) Many amines and diamines have pungent, unpleasant smells. For example, the smell of rotting fish is partly due to ethylamine, $C_2H_5NH_2$. Amines form alkaline solutions in water.

(i) Copy and complete the following equation for the reaction of ethylamine with water

$C_2H_5NH_2(aq) + H_2O(l) \rightleftharpoons$ .... + ... [2]

(ii) Explain how the amine group behaves as a *base*. [3]

> Use the definition of the term *base* in your answer.

(f) What steps can be taken during the production and use of a polymer such as nylon-6,6 to minimise any impact it may have on the environment? [3]

[Total: 30]

The Thread of Life (TL)

3 The structure of the silk produced by web-weaving spiders is of great interest to scientists. Spiders' silk is exceptionally strong yet elastic. Experiments have shown that the protein in the silk is made up mainly of glycine and alanine with small amounts of other amino acids.

glycine   *alanine*

   (a) The protein structure of spiders' silk can be investigated in the laboratory by breaking it down into its constituent amino acids. The resulting mixture can then be investigated by paper chromatography.

      (i) Give the reagent and conditions for breaking down a protein into its constituent amino acids. [2]

      (ii) Name a suitable locating agent for identifying the amino acids on the chromatogram. [1]

   (b) Proteins have three levels of structure: *primary*, *secondary* and *tertiary*. Describe what is meant by each of these terms. [3]

   (c) Alanine exists as two optical isomers (or enantiomers).

      (i) Explain why alanine can exist as two optical isomers. [2]

> Use wedges and dotted lines to represent 3D shapes.

      (ii) Draw three-dimensional structures to show how the two isomers are related. [2]

   (d) **(i)** Draw the structure of the dipeptide produced, GlyAla, when one molecule of glycine reacts with one molecule of alanine. [2]

      (ii) On the structure you have drawn in **(d) (i)**, circle the peptide link. [1]

   (e) Recent research has shown that the presence of another amino acid, proline, makes the silk softer and more flexible. Suggest how the presence of proline might lead to the silk being less crystalline.

proline

[2]

[Total: 15]

4 Hydrogen peroxide is a waste product of many of the reactions that take place in living cells. The enzyme catalase causes the breakdown of hydrogen peroxide into less harmful products.

$$2H_2O_2(aq) \xrightarrow{\text{catalase}} 2H_2O(l) + O_2(g)$$

   (a) The rate of the reaction represented by this equation can be investigated by measuring the amount of oxygen produced as time goes on.

      (i) Draw a labelled diagram of the laboratory apparatus you would use for this experiment. [3]

      (ii) What is meant by the term *rate of reaction*? [2]

   (b) An investigation to measure the rate of this reaction gave the following results.

Experiment	Initial [H_2O_2] (mol dm^{-3})	Initial rate ($\times 10^{-5}$ mol s^{-1})
1	0.10	0.42
2	0.20	0.88
3	0.30	1.30
4	0.40	1.71

> Use the data in your explanation.

      (i) Give the order of the reaction with respect to hydrogen peroxide. Use the data above to explain your answer. [3]

      (ii) The reaction was found to be first order with respect to catalase. Write a rate equation for the overall reaction. [2]

      (iii) State the units of the rate constant for the reaction. [1]

> To gain full marks, your answer should be carefully sequenced.

      (iv) At high concentrations of hydrogen peroxide, the order of the reaction with respect to hydrogen peroxide is found to be zero. Explain why.

QWC: In your answer, you should make it clear how your explanation links to the evidence. [4]

[Total: 15]

The Steel Story (SS)

5 Iron is one of the most widely used transition metals. It is used for a variety of construction purposes in the form of steel, but it is also used, as iron, as a catalyst in some industrial processes.

(a) **(i)** Explain why iron is referred to as a *transition metal*. [2]

(ii) Copy and complete the electron structures for each of the iron species listed below:

Fe $1s^2 2s^2 2p^6 3s^2 3p^6 \dots$
Fe^{2+} $1s^2 2s^2 2p^6 3s^2 3p^6 \dots$
Fe^{3+} $1s^2 2s^2 2p^6 3s^2 3p^6 \dots$ [3]

(iii) Use your answer to **(a) (ii)** to explain why Fe^{3+} ions are more stable than Fe^{2+} ions. [2]

(b) Iron and iron compounds are still used as heterogeneous catalysts in the production of ammonia. Explain why iron and its compounds are catalytically active. [2]

(c) Brown stains of rust are often seen on and around the steel pipes in chemical plants. Rusting is an electrochemical process.

The standard electrode potentials for two relevant half-reactions are given below:

$Fe^{2+}(aq) + 2e^- \rightarrow Fe(s)$ $E^{\ominus} = -0.44\,V$

$\frac{1}{2}O_2(g) + H_2O(l) + 2e^- \rightarrow 2OH^-(aq)$ $E^{\ominus} = +0.40\,V$

(i) Use these equations to write the overall equation for the reaction that occurs as iron starts to corrode. Include state symbols in your answer. [4]

(ii) Calculate the value for $E^{\ominus}_{cell}$ for the electrochemical cell constructed from the two half-cells represented by the equations. [1]

(iii) Describe and explain **one** approach that could be used to prevent the corrosion of steel pipes. [3]

(d) The corrosion of steel pipes can also cause a problem for some industrial processes if the concentration of iron in the solutions passing through the pipes becomes too high.

The concentrations of iron(II) and iron(III) ions are often monitored by titration. Any iron(III) ions present are first reduced to iron(II) ions, and then a sample is titrated with acidified potassium manganate(VII) solution. The equation for the titration reaction is:

$5Fe^{2+}(aq) + MnO_4^-(aq) + 8H^+(aq) \rightarrow 5Fe^{3+}(aq) + Mn^{2+}(aq) + 4H_2O(l)$

(i) $10.0\,cm^3$ of an iron(II) solution is titrated with a $0.0150\,mol\,dm^{-3}$ MnO_4^- solution.
The average titre is $17.80\,cm^3$. Calculate the concentration of the iron(II) solution.
Give your answer to an **appropriate** number of significant figures. [4]

(ii) Describe how you would identify the end-point of the titration. [1]

(e) Another method for determining the concentration of iron in solution is to use colorimetry. Any iron(II) ions are first oxidised to iron(III) and then the solution is reacted with thiocyanate ions. This produces an iron–thiocyanate complex in solution, which is deep red in colour.

(i) Explain why iron–thiocyanate solutions are red. [2]

(ii) Describe how you would use a colorimeter to determine the concentration of Fe^{3+} ions in a sample of water.
QWC: In your answer you should make clear the sequence of steps in the process. [7]

(f) Describe **two** advantages and **one** problem involved in recycling the steel recovered when pipework in chemical plants is replaced. [3]

[Total: 34]

Agriculture and Industry (AI)

UNIT **F335**

Successfully producing crops depends on many factors. The chemistry of some of these, such as soil composition, nutrients and pesticides, are studied in this module. 'CI' refers to sections of your *Chemical Ideas* textbook. 'Storylines' refers to your *Chemical Storylines* textbook.

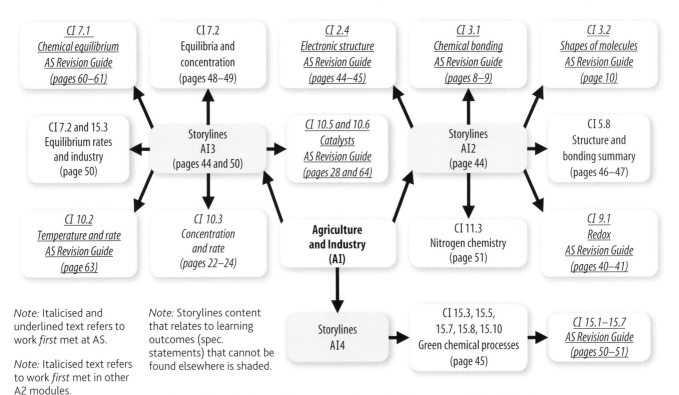

CI 7.1
Chemical equilibrium
AS Revision Guide
(pages 60–61)

CI 7.2
Equilibria and
concentration
(pages 48–49)

CI 2.4
Electronic structure
AS Revision Guide
(pages 44–45)

CI 3.1
Chemical bonding
AS Revision Guide
(pages 8–9)

CI 3.2
Shapes of molecules
AS Revision Guide
(page 10)

CI 7.2 and 15.3
Equilibrium rates
and industry
(page 50)

Storylines
AI3
(pages 44 and 50)

CI 10.5 and 10.6
Catalysts
AS Revision Guide
(pages 28 and 64)

Storylines
AI2
(page 44)

CI 5.8
Structure and
bonding summary
(pages 46–47)

CI 10.2
Temperature and rate
AS Revision Guide
(page 63)

CI 10.3
Concentration
and rate
(pages 22–24)

**Agriculture
and Industry
(AI)**

CI 11.3
Nitrogen chemistry
(page 51)

CI 9.1
Redox
AS Revision Guide
(pages 40–41)

Storylines
AI4

CI 15.3, 15.5,
15.7, 15.8, 15.10
Green chemical processes
(page 45)

CI 15.1–15.7
AS Revision Guide
(pages 50–51)

Note: Italicised and underlined text refers to work *first* met at AS.

Note: Italicised text refers to work *first* met in other A2 modules.

Note: Storylines content that relates to learning outcomes (spec. statements) that cannot be found elsewhere is shaded.

From *Chemical Storylines* you will need to be aware of the following.

Improving food production (Storylines AI2, 3, 4)

There are risks and benefits to all of these processes.

Plants need the right conditions to grow well:

- Fertilisers add nutrients for plant growth (such as NO_3^-, PO_4^{3-}, K^+).
- Manure adds organic matter for plant growth and soil improvement.
- Lime or chalk added to the soil will alter the pH of the soil.
- Pesticides (insecticides, fungicides and weedkillers) can increase crop yields. They need to be biodegradable so they do not accumulate in food chains.
- GM (genetically modified) crops can be developed to give crops with desirable properties.

Percentage yields (Chemical Ideas 15.7)

You can revise percentage yields calculations using *Revise AS Chemistry for Salters*, page 52.

These calculations apply to both industrial reactions and organic synthesis. They are essential information for choosing the best industrial method of production, in conjunction with information about atom economy.

Green chemical processes

Chemical Ideas 15.3, 15.7, 15.8, 15.10

Risks and benefits

You need to be able to discuss the risks and benefits for a given chemical process in terms of hazards associated with raw materials, reactants, products and by-products, explosions, acidic gases, flammable gases and toxic emissions (where appropriate).

Which type of reaction has the greatest atom economy?

> You have already met the idea of atom economy on page 7.

Rearrangement reactions

For example, the isomerisation of alkanes to make higher octane petrol:

$$CH_3CH_2CH_2CH_2CH_2CH_3 \rightarrow CH_3C(CH_3)_2CH_2CH_3 \quad \text{\% atom economy} = 100\%.$$
$$M_r = 86.0 \qquad\qquad\qquad M_r = 86.0$$

> atom economy
> $$= \frac{M_r \text{ useful product}}{\text{total } M_r \text{ reactants}} \times 100$$

Addition reactions

For example, the manufacture of ethanol from ethene:

$$CH_2{=}CH_2 \quad + \quad H_2O \quad \rightarrow \quad CH_3CH_2OH \quad \text{\% atom economy} = 100\%$$
$$M_r = 28.0 \qquad\quad M_r = 18.0 \qquad\quad M_r = 46.0$$

Substitution reactions

For example, the production of a halogenoalkane from an alcohol:

$$\text{---OH} + \text{HCl} \longrightarrow \text{---Cl} + H_2O$$
$$M_r = 74.0 \quad M_r = 36.5 \qquad M_r = 92.5 \quad M_r = 18.0$$

Total M_r of reactants = 110.5; M_r of useful product = 92.5

$$\text{\% atom economy} = \frac{92.5}{110.5} \times 100 = 83.7\%$$

> Most substitution reactions have a lower atom economy than this.

Elimination reactions

For example, the preparation of an alkene from an alcohol:

$$CH_3CH_2CH_2OH \quad \rightarrow \quad CH_3CH{=}CH_2 \quad + \quad H_2O$$
$$M_r = 60.0 \qquad\qquad M_r = 42.0 \qquad M_r = 18.0$$

Total M_r of reactants = 60.0; M_r of useful product = 42.0

$$\text{\% atom economy} = \frac{42.0}{60.0} \times 100 = 70.0\%$$

> If an industrial process is designed so that reactions with high atom economy are used then this will reduce waste products and use less feedstock.

Recycling of materials

The principles of green chemistry are:

- minimise waste
- reduce energy consumption
- reduce feedstock consumption.

> You may be asked to apply these principles to specific examples.

QUICK CHECK QUESTIONS

1 Explain what a substitution reaction is.
2 Why does an addition reaction have a higher atom economy than an elimination reaction?
3 What particular difficulties are there in recycling plastics?
4 Calculate the atom economy for the manufacture of phosphoric(V) acid:
$$Ca_3(PO_4)_2 + 3H_2SO_4 \rightarrow 3CaSO_4 + 2H_3PO_4$$
5 Why does the recycling of aluminium result in such a large saving in carbon dioxide emitted, when compared with the recycling of other materials such as glass?

Bonding, structure and properties: a summary

Chemical Ideas 5.8

The properties of materials are determined by:

- the types of particles in the material – e.g. atoms, ions or molecules
- the bonding in the material – e.g. covalent, ionic, metallic, intermolecular bonds
- the structure present in the material – e.g. giant lattice, molecular or macromolecular.

	GIANT LATTICE			COVALENT MOLECULAR	
	Ionic	Covalent network	Metallic	Simple molecular	Macromolecular
What substances have this type of structure?	compounds of metals with non-metals	some elements in Group 4 and some of their compounds	metals	some non-metal elements and some non-metal/non-metal compounds	polymers
Examples	sodium chloride, NaCl; calcium oxide, CaO	diamond C; graphite, C; silica, SiO$_2$	sodium, Na; copper, Cu; iron, Fe	carbon dioxide, CO$_2$; chlorine, Cl$_2$; water, H$_2$O	poly(ethene), nylon, proteins, DNA
What type of particles does it contain?	ions	atoms	positive ions surrounded by delocalised electrons	small molecules	long-chain molecules
How are the particles bonded together?	strong ionic bonds; attraction between oppositely charged ions	strong covalent bonds	strong metallic bonds; attraction of atoms' nuclei for delocalised electrons	weak intermolecular bonds between molecules; strong covalent bonds between the atoms within each molecule	weak intermolecular bonds between molecules; strong covalent bonds between the atoms within each molecule
What are the typical properties?					
Melting point and boiling point	high	very high	generally high (except mercury)	low	moderate (often decompose on heating)
Hardness	hard but brittle	very hard (if 3D)	hard but malleable	soft	variable; many are soft but often flexible
Electrical conductivity	conduct when molten or dissolved in water; electrolytes	do not normally conduct (except graphite)	conduct when solid or liquid	do not conduct	do not normally conduct
Solubility in water	often soluble	insoluble	insoluble (but some react)	usually insoluble, unless molecules contain groups which can hydrogen bond with water	usually insoluble
Solubility in non-polar solvents (e.g. hexane)	generally insoluble	insoluble	insoluble	usually soluble	sometimes soluble

The Periodic Table allows trends in bonding, structure and properties to be recognised. For example, for the first 20 elements of the Periodic Table:

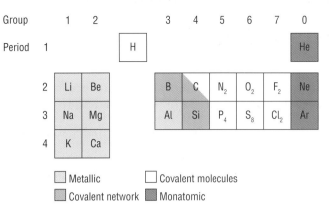

You can visualise the different types of structures as follows:

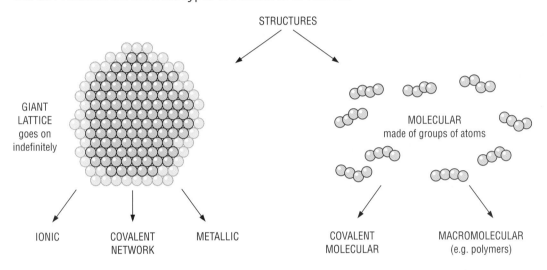

STRUCTURES

GIANT LATTICE goes on indefinitely

MOLECULAR made of groups of atoms

IONIC   COVALENT NETWORK   METALLIC   COVALENT MOLECULAR   MACROMOLECULAR (e.g. polymers)

QUICK CHECK QUESTIONS

1 Use the tables in this section to give a structure for each of the following:
   (a) vanadium
   (b) xenon
   (c) cotton
   (d) potassium iodide
   (e) propan-1-ol
   (f) steel
   (g) glass
   (h) polyester
   (i) lead(II) nitrate(V)
   (j) silicon carbide
   (k) iodine.

2 For each substance listed in question **1**, give the following properties:
   (a) state at room temperature (solid, liquid or gas)
   (b) solubility in water (soluble or insoluble)
   (c) electrical conductivity (high or low).

3 Draw a diagram to show the bonding in magnesium.

4 Compare and contrast the intramolecular and intermolecular bonding in:
   (a) water and nylon
   (b) hexane and hydrogen sulfide.

Equilibria and concentrations

Chemical Ideas 7.2

a and *b* are the number of moles of reactants A and B; *c* and *d* are the number of moles of products C and D.

Consider the general equilibrium reaction:

$$aA(aq) + bB(aq) \rightleftharpoons cC(aq) + dD(aq)$$

The **equilibrium law** states that:

$$K_c = \frac{[C]^c [D]^d}{[A]^a [B]^b}$$

Remember – products divided by reactants!

You will come across other equilibrium constants, such as K_a in connection with weak acids.

This constant, K_c, is the **equilibrium constant** for the reaction at a specified temperature. The letter K is used to represent all equilibrium constants. When the expression is written in terms of concentrations, we write K_c.

For example, for the equilibrium reaction:

$$N_2(g) + 3H_2(g) \rightleftharpoons 2NH_3(g)$$

$$K_c = \frac{[NH_3]^2}{[N_2] [H_2]^3}$$

The square brackets indicate the concentration in $mol\,dm^{-3}$ of whatever is inside the brackets.

K_c is a measure of *how far* a reaction proceeds. If an equilibrium mixture is composed largely of reactants, then the value of K_c is small; if the equilibrium mixture is composed largely of products, then the value of K_c is large.

Units of K_c

Units for K_c need to be calculated in every case.

It is easy to forget about the units of K_c.

WORKED EXAMPLE

$$K_c = \frac{[NH_3]^2}{[N_2] [H_2]^3}$$

It may be that K_c has no units at all.

$$\text{units} = \frac{(mol\,dm^{-3})^2}{(mol\,dm^{-3})(mol\,dm^{-3})^3}$$

$$= \frac{1}{(mol\,dm^{-3})^2}$$

$$= mol^{-2}\,dm^6$$

Calculations involving K_c

WORKED EXAMPLE 1

Calculate the value of K_c at 763 K for the reaction $H_2(g) + I_2(g) \rightleftharpoons 2HI(g)$ given the following data:

$$[H_2(g)] = 1.92\,mol\,dm^{-3}, [I_2(g)] = 3.63\,mol\,dm^{-3} \text{ and } [HI(g)] = 17.8\,mol\,dm^{-3}$$

$$K_c = \frac{[HI]^2}{[H_2] [I_2]}$$

$$= \frac{(17.8\,mol\,dm^{-3})^2}{1.92\,mol\,dm^{-3} \times 3.63\,mol\,dm^{-3}}$$

$$= 45.5 \text{ (no units)}$$

WORKED EXAMPLE 2

You can also calculate the composition of equilibrium mixtures.

$$CH_3COOH(l) + C_2H_5OH(l) \rightleftharpoons CH_3COOC_2H_5(l) + H_2O(l)$$

K_c for the above esterification reaction has a value of 4.10 at 25 °C. Calculate the equilibrium concentration of ethyl ethanoate, given that $[CH_3COOH(l)] = 0.255\,mol\,dm^{-3}$, $[C_2H_5OH(l)] = 0.245\,mol\,dm^{-3}$ and $[H_2O(l)] = 0.437\,mol\,dm^{-3}$.

$$K_c = \frac{[CH_3COOC_2H_5(l)]\,[H_2O(l)]}{[CH_3COOH(l)]\,[C_2H_5OH(l)]}$$

Substituting the values into the expression for K_c:

$$4.10 = \frac{[CH_3COOC_2H_5(l)] \times 0.437\,mol\,dm^{-3}}{0.255\,mol\,dm^{-3} \times 0.245\,mol\,dm^{-3}}$$

Rearranging the expression:

$$[CH_3COOC_2H_5(l)] = \frac{4.10 \times 0.255\,mol\,dm^{-3} \times 0.245\,mol\,dm^{-3}}{0.437\,mol\,dm^{-3}} = 0.586\,mol\,dm^{-3}$$

> Remember – if data is given to 3 significant figures, you should give your answer to 3 significant figures.

What affects the value of K_c?

The *only* thing that affects the numerical value of K_c is a change in *temperature*.

	Exothermic reactions	Endothermic reactions
Temperature increases	value of K_c decreases	value of K_c increases
Temperature decreases	value of K_c increases	value of K_c decreases

QUICK CHECK QUESTIONS

1 Write expressions for K_c for the following reversible reactions. Include the units of K_c.
   (a) $2SO_2(g) + O_2(g) \rightleftharpoons 2SO_3(g)$
   (b) $N_2O_4(g) \rightleftharpoons 2NO_2(g)$

2 Calculate the value of K_c for the Haber process reaction, $3H_2(g) + N_2(g) \rightleftharpoons 2NH_3(g)$ at 1000 K, given $[H_2(g)] = 1.84\,mol\,dm^{-3}$, $[N_2(g)] = 1.36\,mol\,dm^{-3}$ and $[NH_3(g)] = 0.142\,mol\,dm^{-3}$.

3 Ethanol is produced in industry by the hydration of ethene, using a phosphoric acid catalyst: $C_2H_4(g) + H_2O(g) \rightleftharpoons C_2H_5OH(g)$. The forward reaction is exothermic.

(a) Explain how increasing the pressure would affect the position of equilibrium and the value of K_c.

(b) Explain how increasing the temperature would affect the position of equilibrium and the value of K_c.

(c) What is the advantage of using a catalyst, in terms of the equilibrium?

4 Calculate the concentration of ethanol at equilibrium in the esterification reaction:
   $C_2H_5OH(l) + CH_3COOH(l) \rightleftharpoons CH_3COOC_2H_5(l) + H_2O(l)$
   given that $K_c = 4.0$, $[CH_3COOH] = 0.80\,mol\,dm^{-3}$ and $[CH_3COOC_2H_5] = [H_2O] = 3.0\,mol\,dm^{-3}$.

Equilibrium, rates and industry

Chemical Ideas 7.2 and 15.3, Storylines AI3

Industrial processes are carried out under precise operating conditions for each part of the process to maximise yield and reduce costs. Many chemical processes that involve a reversible reaction use conditions that do not allow the reaction to reach equilibrium – the amount of product manufactured per unit time is much more important. Unconverted reactants can often be recycled.

Manufacture of ammonia (Haber Process)

The raw materials are air and natural gas. From these, a feedstock of nitrogen and hydrogen (ratio 1:3) is made.

$$N_2(g) + 3H_2(g) \rightleftharpoons 2NH_3(g) \qquad \Delta H = -92\,kJ\,mol^{-1}$$

> Unreacted nitrogen and hydrogen can be recovered and recycled.

The usual conditions for this process are: iron catalyst, temperature 450 °C and 200 atm pressure. These represent compromise values in order to produce a reasonable yield at an acceptable rate of attainment of equilibrium.

Increasing the temperature speeds up the rate at which equilibrium is achieved (more molecules have the necessary activation energy when they collide), but decreases the yield (position of equilibrium moves to the left because the forward reaction is exothermic).

> Don't panic if an examination question uses an industrial process which is new to you. There will be enough information in the question for you to use chemical ideas on rates, equilibrium etc.

Increasing the pressure increases both the yield (position of equilibrium moves to the right, where there are fewer moles of gas) and the rate (more collisions), but it is expensive (capital costs of the high-pressure plant) and the running costs (electricity) are high. Using a catalyst speeds up the rate at which equilibrium is achieved.

How does K_c change?

> Temperature is the only factor to alter K_c.

Change	Position of equilibrium	K_c	Rate
Concentrations	changed	unchanged	changed
Total pressure	may change	unchanged	may change
Temperature	changed	changed	changed
Catalyst used	unchanged	unchanged	changed

QUICK CHECK QUESTIONS

1 What conditions would give the greatest yield of nitrogen dioxide?

$$N_2O_4(g) \rightleftharpoons 2NO_2(g) \qquad \Delta H = +57\,kJ\,mol^{-1}$$

2 In the manufacture of sulfuric acid, the first step is to oxidise sulfur(IV) oxide:

$$2SO_2(g) + O_2(g) \rightleftharpoons 2SO_3(g) \qquad \Delta H = -205\,kJ\,mol^{-1}$$

The conditions used are: vanadium(V) oxide catalyst, 1 atm pressure and 500 °C.
Give reasons for the conditions used.

3 In the first step in the manufacture of hydrogen from natural gas, methane is mixed with steam and a limited supply of oxygen. This mixture is passed over a catalyst of nickel at 900 °C and the following two reactions occur:

$$CH_4(g) + H_2O(g) \rightleftharpoons CO(g) + 3H_2(g) \quad \text{endothermic}$$
$$2CH_4(g) + O_2(g) \rightarrow 2CO(g) + 4H_2(g) \quad \text{exothermic}$$

(a) Why is oxygen added to the mixture of methane and steam?

(b) Would an increase in pressure be justified? Give reasons for your answer.

(c) The carbon monoxide produced is then converted to carbon dioxide and more hydrogen, using an iron catalyst:

$$CO(g) + H_2O(g) \rightleftharpoons CO_2(g) + H_2(g) \quad \text{exothermic}$$

State and explain what temperature would be suitable for this reaction.

(d) How could the carbon dioxide be removed from the mixture?

Nitrogen chemistry

Chemical Ideas 11.3

Group 5 is in the middle of the p block in the Periodic Table, with all the elements having electron configurations ending with p^3 (e.g. nitrogen is $1s^2\,2s^2\,2p^3$).

Nitrogen gas consists of diatomic molecules ($N\equiv N$), which are very unreactive because of the extremely high activation energy needed to start breaking bonds.

The Periodic Table can be found on the inside front cover of this book.

Nitrogen cycle

This cycle involves natural redox reactions involving interconversions between nitrogen species in the soil and/or the atmosphere.

Nitrogen species	Formula	Oxidation state	Action producing the species
Nitrogen gas	$N_2(g)$	0	Denitrifying bacteria in soil
Nitrate(V) ion	$NO_3^-(aq)$	+5	Nitrifying bacteria in soil
Nitrate(III) ion	$NO_2^-(aq)$	+3	Nitrifying bacteria in soil
Ammonium ion	$NH_4^+(aq)$	−3	Root nodules in legumes. Bacteria and microorganisms in soil
Dinitrogen(I) oxide [nitrous oxide]	$N_2O(g)$	+1	Denitrifying bacteria in soil
Nitrogen(II) oxide [nitrogen monoxide]	$NO(g)$	+2	Car engines, thunderstorms, denitrifying bacteria in soil
Nitrogen (IV) oxide [nitrogen dioxide]	$NO_2(g)$	+4	Oxidation of NO in atmosphere

N_2O and NO are both colourless gases, whereas NO_2 is a brown gas at room temperature.

The bonding in, and shapes of, some common nitrogen-containing species are shown below:

	ammonia	ammonium ion	nitrate(III) ion	nitrate(V) ion
bonding	H ̈N̈ H (with H below)	[H ̈N̈ H with H below]+	[O ̈N̈ O]−	[O ̈N̈ O with O below]−
shape	H–N–H with H (pyramid)	[H–N–H with H]+ (tetrahedral)	[O–N–O]− (bent)	[O–N–O with O]− (triangular planar)
	pyramid	tetrahedral	bent	triangular planar

QUICK CHECK QUESTIONS

1 (a) Write an equation and describe what you would see if nitrogen(II) oxide was mixed with air.
   (b) What are the changes in oxidation state of the elements involved?
2 Instead of growing legumes, how could an organic farmer increase the concentration of nitrate(V) ions in soil?

3 In addition to those in the above table, what two processes remove nutrients, such as nitrogen compounds, from the soil?
4 Which type of soil bacteria carries out oxidation? Explain your answer.

Colour by Design (CD)

In this module you will discover what causes colour. The module explores the restoration of an oil painting, and the associated chemistry and analytical techniques needed to carry this out. The module also looks at the development of synthetic dyes for cloth. 'CI' refers to sections of your *Chemical Ideas* textbook. 'Storylines' refers to your *Chemical Storylines* textbook.

Note: Italicised and underlined text refers to work *first* met at AS.

Note: Italicised text refers to work *first* met in other A2 modules.

Note: Storylines content that relates to learning outcomes (spec. statements) that cannot be found elsewhere is shaded.

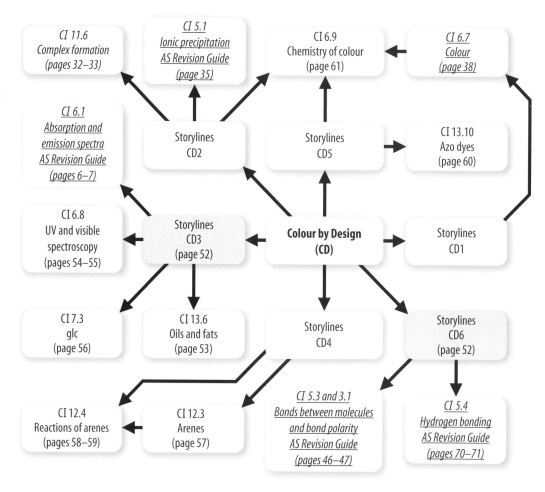

CI 11.6
Complex formation
(pages 32–33)

CI 5.1
Ionic precipitation
AS Revision Guide
(page 35)

CI 6.9
Chemistry of colour
(page 61)

CI 6.7
Colour
(page 38)

CI 6.1
Absorption and
emission spectra
AS Revision Guide
(pages 6–7)

Storylines
CD2

Storylines
CD5

CI 13.10
Azo dyes
(page 60)

CI 6.8
UV and visible
spectroscopy
(pages 54–55)

Storylines
CD3
(page 52)

**Colour by Design
(CD)**

Storylines
CD1

CI 7.3
glc
(page 56)

CI 13.6
Oils and fats
(page 53)

Storylines
CD4

Storylines
CD6
(page 52)

CI 12.4
Reactions of arenes
(pages 58–59)

CI 12.3
Arenes
(page 57)

CI 5.3 and 3.1
Bonds between molecules
and bond polarity
AS Revision Guide
(pages 46–47)

CI 5.4
Hydrogen bonding
AS Revision Guide
(pages 70–71)

From *Chemical Storylines* you will need to be aware of the following.

Atomic emission spectroscopy (Storyline CD3)

Laser microspectral analysis (LMA) is used to produce a type of emission spectrum to analyse pigment samples.

Attaching dyes to fibres (Storyline CD6)

Make sure that you are familiar with diagrams showing these ways of attaching dyes to fibres.

The stronger the bond between fabric and dye, the more colourfast the dye will be.

- Direct dyes attach to cotton via hydrogen bonds.
- Acid dyes attach to protein fibres, e.g. silk via ionic bonds.
- Other dyes attach to fabrics using a mordant – this forms a complex, linking fibre and dye together.
- Fibre-reactive dyes form strong covalent bonds with cotton fabrics.

Oils and fats

Chemical Ideas 13.6

Oils and fats are naturally occurring **triesters** of propane-1,2,3-triol (glycerol) and long-chain carboxylic acids (fatty acids). Each of the three ester groups can be from the same fatty acid or they can be different (mixed triester).

Fatty acids

'Fatty acids' are the carboxylic acids in fats and oils. They have an even number of carbons (typically 16 or 18) in their unbranched carbon chain. These chains can be either saturated (contain only single C—C bonds) or unsaturated (contain some double C=C bonds). Typical saturated and unsaturated fatty acid are shown below:

stearic acid
Saturated – no double C=C bonds

linoleic acid
Unsaturated – two double C=C bonds

Any natural oil or fat contains a mixture of triesters. Triesters from largely saturated fatty acids are solids or fats – there is better packing of the molecules resulting in stronger intermolecular bonds. Triesters from largely unsaturated fatty acids are liquids or oils.

H
|
H—C—O—H
|
H—C—O—H
|
H—C—O—H
|
H

propane-1,2,3-triol (glycerol)

> Triesters are compounds containing three ester groups.

Hydrolysis (saponification) of esters

Any natural oil or fat can be broken down into the sodium salt of the fatty acid (soap) and glycerol by heating with dilute sodium hydroxide solution.

triester formed from glycerol and palmitic acid + 3Na⁺OH⁻ ⟶ glycerol + 3 sodium palmitate

triester formed from
glycerol and palmitic acid

glycerol

sodium palmitate

> If the free acid is required, it can be released by treating the sodium salt with dilute hydrochloric acid.

> You have already looked at the hydrolysis of esters on page 6.

Hydrogenation (reduction or addition)

Addition of hydrogen to unsaturated oils, using a nickel catalyst and the correct conditions, produces a more saturated solid fat, which can be used in the manufacture of margarine. Not all the C=C double bonds are hydrogenated and this gives a spreadable fat, which is still polyunsaturated.

> This is an example of heterogeneous catalysis.

QUICK CHECK QUESTIONS

1 What are the bond angles around the carbon–carbon double bond in an unsaturated oil?
2 How does the shape of a saturated triester molecule differ from that of an unsaturated triester molecule?
3 Why are saturated fats solids?
4 Draw the skeletal formula for the fat made from stearic acid, $CH_3(CH_2)_{16}COOH$.
5 How would you decide if an oil was linseed oil or not?
6 The degree of unsaturation can be determined by measuring the mass of iodine which reacts with 100 g of oil or fat. Explain why this is the case.

Ultraviolet and visible spectroscopy

Chemical Ideas 6.8

Absorption of ultraviolet and visible light

You can remind yourself about colour by reading page 38.

If visible light falls on a coloured solution, some wavelengths are absorbed and some are transmitted. What we see are the transmitted wavelengths (colours). Many molecules also absorb ultraviolet (UV) radiation. Because our eyes don't detect UV light, a molecule that absorbs only UV light (and transmits all visible wavelengths) appears colourless.

Electronic transitions and unsaturated molecules

Absorption of UV or visible light causes **electronic transitions** in molecules – electrons move to higher energy levels and the molecule becomes 'excited'. Many unsaturated molecules (those with C=C bonds or benzene rings) and those with **conjugated** systems absorb UV and visible light. The **delocalised** electrons in these systems require slightly less energy to become excited compared with electrons in single bonds.

A conjugated system has alternate C=C and C—C bonds. Benzene rings and N=N bonds can also be part of conjugated systems.

Carotene is an example of a large conjugated molecule.

carotene

Blue and green light are absorbed so the carotene appears orange in white light.

UV–visible spectroscopy

UV radiation has wavelengths between 280 and 400 nm. It has higher energy than visible radiation.

In UV and visible spectroscopy, the **spectrometer** scans a range of wavelengths of both UV and visible light. The instrument produces a **spectrum** such as the one shown below for carotene:

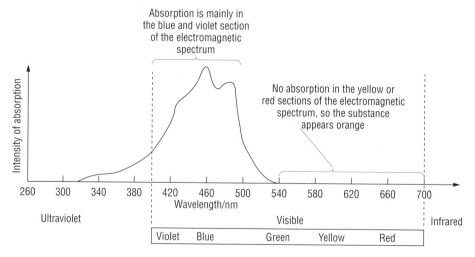

Notice the following features of the spectrum:

$1\,nm = 1 \times 10^{-9}\,m$

- the x-axis shows wavelength, measured in nanometres (nm)
- the y-axis shows intensity of absorption; usually there are no units
- unlike an infrared spectrum, the trace from a UV–visible spectrum is much broader. It is the overall shape of the spectrum that is important rather than individual peaks.

Interpreting the spectrum

To identify the colour of a test solution, you find the wavelength at which absorption is greatest – this is known as λ_{max}.

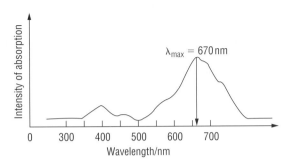

Absorption is more intense and the wavelength of λ_{max} increases for organic molecules with large delocalised systems.

For example, in the spectrum above, λ_{max} is at 670 nm. This is the wavelength of red light – so the colour of the solution will be the complementary colour of red, which is blue/green. Using a colour wheel will help you to find the complementary colour.

You can see a colour wheel on page 38.

Reflectance spectra

UV and visible spectrometry is also used when analysing substances that cannot easily be made into a solution. UV and visible light is shone onto the surface of the sample and any reflected light is collected and analysed – the result is a **reflectance spectrum**. One area where this technique is used is in the analysis of pigments from old paintings.

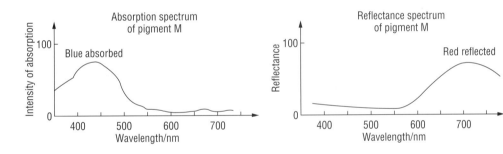

Compare the absorption and reflectance spectra of the pigment above. Where there is a peak in the absorption spectrum, there is a trough in the reflectance spectrum, and vice versa.

QUICK CHECK QUESTIONS

1   Study the absorption and reflectance spectra of pigment M above. Suggest, with reasons, the likely colour of the pigment.

2   Draw the absorption spectrum of a yellow/green pigment.

3   Explain why there are many shades of blue.

4   Describe the absorption spectrum of a grey pigment.

5   Explain how chlorophyll makes plant leaves appear green in white light.

Gas–liquid chromatography

Chemical Ideas 7.3

There are many different types of chromatography – paper, thin-layer, column, gas–liquid and high-pressure (performance) liquid chromatography.

There are details about thin-layer chromatography on page vi.

Nitrogen and noble gases are used as inert carrier gases.

An alternative to a packed column, is a very long and very thin capillary tube with a high boiling point liquid coating on the inside surface.

Chromatography is a method of separating and identifying the components of a mixture – e.g. the components that make up the oils used in painting.

All types of chromatography depend on the equilibrium set up when the components of a mixture distribute themselves between the **stationary phase** and the **mobile phase**. Components with a higher affinity for the stationary phase move more slowly than those with a lower affinity.

In gas–liquid chromatography (g.l.c.), the stationary phase is a non-volatile liquid coated on the surface of finely divided solid particles. This material is packed inside a long thin **column**, which is coiled inside an oven. An unreactive **carrier gas** acts as the mobile phase and carries the mixture through the column.

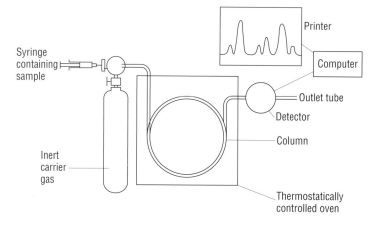

As each component emerges from the column, a peak is recorded on the **chromatogram**. The *area* under each peak is proportional to the amount of that component in the mixture. The *time* that a component takes to emerge is called the **retention time**.

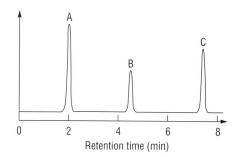

Compound	Retention time
A	2 min
B	4.5 min
C	7.4 min

QUICK CHECK QUESTIONS

1 What would be the effect on the retention time of increasing the flow rate of the carrier gas?

2 Often the outlet from a g.l.c. instrument is connected to a mass spectrometer. As a result, what extra information could be obtained about the mixture?

3 (a) When analysing the oils in paintings, why are the methyl esters of fatty acids used to run g.l.c. traces, rather than the acids themselves?

   (b) How can the relative amounts of each component be calculated?

Arenes

Chemical Ideas 12.3

The simplest arene is benzene, C_6H_6, which has a flat hexagonal structure with a bond angle of 120°.

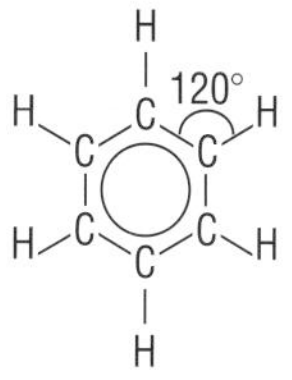

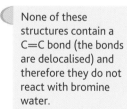

C_6H_5 is called 'phenyl'.

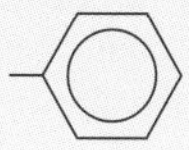

Arenes are hydrocarbons that contain benzene rings. Their names always end in -ene, meaning that they are unsaturated (as in alk*ene*).

All carbon–carbon bond lengths are the same (0.139 nm), with a value between that of a single and double bond. This means that one electron from each carbon is delocalised over the whole ring.

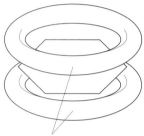

Regions of higher electron density above and below the benzene ring

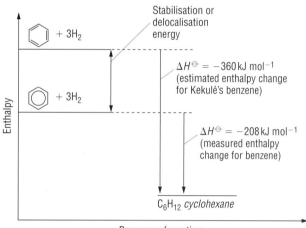

Stabilisation or delocalisation energy

$\Delta H^\ominus = -360\,kJ\,mol^{-1}$ (estimated enthalpy change for Kekulé's benzene)

$\Delta H^\ominus = -208\,kJ\,mol^{-1}$ (measured enthalpy change for benzene)

C_6H_{12} cyclohexane

Enthalpy

Progress of reaction

This arrangement is much more stable than an alternate single/double bond arrangement, as demonstrated by the enthalpy change diagram on the right:

Various models have been used to explain the bonding in benzene and aromatic compounds. Some of these were ridiculed at first, but chemists gradually realised that each model has its advantages and disadvantages. The real picture is a combination of the models.

When naming substituted benzenes, use the lowest numbers possible and list the groups in alphabetical order.

None of these structures contain a C=C bond (the bonds are delocalised) and therefore they do not react with bromine water.

Other examples of arenes (aromatic hydrocarbons) include:

methylbenzene

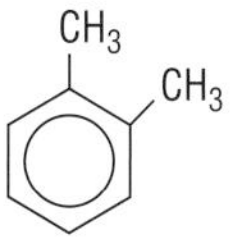

1,2-dimethylbenzene

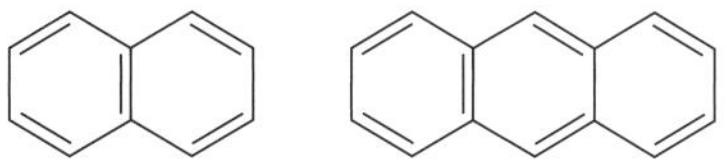

naphthalene ($C_{10}H_8$)

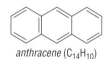

anthracene ($C_{14}H_{10}$)

QUICK CHECK QUESTIONS

1 Draw the structures of
   (a) 1,3,5-trimethylbenzene
   (b) phenylethene.
2 What chemical test could be used to distinguish between compounds (a) and (b) in question 1? What would you see?
3 How many electrons are delocalised in
   (a) benzene
   (b) naphthalene?

4 According to the enthalpy diagram for the hydrogenation of benzene above, what is the magnitude of the delocalisation energy for benzene?
5 Draw the skeletal formulae for the four isomers of dimethylbenzene and name them.
6 Describe what Kekulé's proposal was for the structure of benzene.

Reactions of arenes

Chemical Ideas 12.4

Benzene is usually represented by

in equations.

Benzene is a planar molecule, with areas of delocalised electron density above and below the plane. These accessible areas of electron density will attract electrophiles.

Unlike alkenes, arenes usually undergo substitution reactions, but very rarely addition reactions. Substitution reactions keep the delocalised electron structure, which makes arenes more stable than alkenes, whereas addition would destroy this. Consequently the vast majority of benzene, and other arene, reactions are **electrophilic substitutions**.

A general equation for these reactions is:

$$R–X + E^+ \rightarrow R–E + X^+$$

Electrophiles are positive ions or molecules with a partial positive charge localised on one of the atoms that will be attracted to a negatively charged region. They react by accepting a pair of electrons to form a covalent bond.

- R is the aryl group
- X is the leaving group
- E^+ is the electrophile.

You need to know about the following examples. Learn the reaction conditions and the reacting electrophile in each case.

Nitration

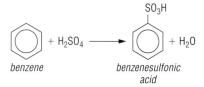

benzene   nitrobenzene

$$O=\overset{+}{N}=O$$

Reagents/conditions: benzene + concentrated nitric acid mixed with concentrated sulfuric acid.

Temperature below 55 °C.

Electrophile: NO_2^+ produced by the reaction:

$$HNO_3 + 2H_2SO_4 \rightarrow NO_2^+ + 2HSO_4^- + H_3O^+$$

Sulfonation

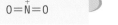

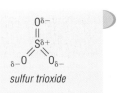

sulfur trioxide

benzene   benzenesulfonic acid

Reagents/conditions: benzene + concentrated sulfuric acid. Heat under reflux for several hours.

Electrophile: SO_3 (present in concentrated sulfuric acid).

Chlorination

benzene   chlorobenzene

Reagents/conditions: benzene + chlorine + anhydrous aluminium chloride. Room temperature.

Electrophile: Cl^+ is produced in the following reaction:

$$Cl_2 + AlCl_3 \rightarrow AlCl_4^- + Cl^+$$

Bromination

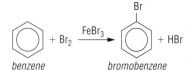

benzene   bromobenzene

Reagents/conditions: benzene + bromine + anhydrous iron(III) bromide or iron filings. Room temperature.

Electrophile: Br^+ is produced in the following reaction:

$$Br_2 + FeBr_3 \rightarrow FeBr_4^- + Br^+$$

Alkylation

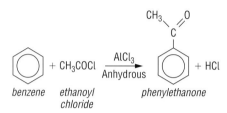

benzene   *ethylbenzene*

Reagents/conditions: benzene + chloroalkane + anhydrous aluminium chloride. Heat under reflux.

Electrophile: $CH_3CH_2{}^{\delta+}—Cl—AlCl_3{}^{\delta-}$ or simply $CH_3CH_2{}^+(AlCl_4{}^-)$, formed by polarisation of the R–Cl bond by the $AlCl_3$

> These alkylation and acylation reactions are known as Friedel–Crafts reactions.

Acylation

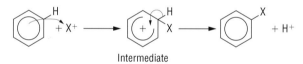

benzene   *ethanoyl chloride*   *phenylethanone*

Reagents/conditions: benzene + acyl chloride + anhydrous aluminium chloride. Heat under reflux.

Electrophile: $CH_3CO^+(AlCl_4)^-$ formed by polarisation of the C—Cl bond by the $AlCl_3$

> Friedel–Crafts reactions are useful in organic synthesis because they add carbon side chains to the benzene ring. These side chains can then be modified further.

Friedel–Crafts

Alkylation and acylation reactions can be carried out in ionic liquids as combination solvent–catalyst systems. These reduce solvent emissions, reduce flammability, often recycle easily and allow reactions to be carried out at reduced temperature.

Electrophilic substitution mechanism

All of the above reactions involve an electrophile attacking the electron-rich arene ring, and forming a new bond with the ring. In order to regain the delocalised system, and restore its stability, one of the original ring hydrogen atoms is lost as a proton.

Intermediate

QUICK CHECK QUESTIONS

1 What term describes the action of concentrated sulfuric acid in the nitrating mixture?
2 Nitration of benzene gives 1,3-dinitrobenzene – write an equation for the reaction, and give all the reagents and reaction conditions.
3 Chlorine and bromine are weak electrophiles. How can their strength as an electrophile be increased?

4 What reagents and conditions are needed to make 2-bromo-1,3-dimethylbenzene in two stages from benzene? (*Hint*: add the methyl groups first and then the bromine.) Write equations for the two stages.
5 (a) Write an equation for the sulfonation of phenylethanone.
   (b) How many isomers of the product could be made?

Azo dyes

Chemical Ideas 13.10

Nitrous acid is unstable and is made as needed by reacting $NaNO_2$ with dilute HCl(aq).

Azo compounds make excellent dyes. They are made by reacting a 'coupling agent' (see below) with a diazonium ion.

The structure and formation of diazonium ions

Diazonium ions have the general formula $R-N^+\equiv N$. Only aromatic diazonium ions are stable, and even these have to be made in solution at temperatures below $5\,^\circ C$.

Learn the reactants and conditions for this reaction, known as **diazotisation** – phenylamine, dilute hydrochloric acid, sodium nitrate(III), at a temperature kept lower than $5\,^\circ C$.

The structure of the benzenediazonium ion and its formation are shown below:

$$\text{\raisebox{0pt}{⬡}}-NH_2 + HNO_2 + H^+ \longrightarrow \text{\raisebox{0pt}{⬡}}-\overset{+}{N}\equiv N + 2H_2O$$

phenylamine   nitrous acid   benzenediazonium ion

The formation of azo compounds

Diazonium ions are weak electrophiles. They will attack phenols and aromatic amines (called **coupling agents**), both of which have especially electron-rich benzene rings. During the reaction, an $-N=N-$ bond is formed. The reaction is called a **coupling reaction** and the compound formed is an **azo compound**.

Azo compounds have the general formula $R-N=N-R$. Compounds in which the R groups are aryl groups are the most stable.

$$\text{⬡}-\overset{+}{N}\equiv N + \text{⬡}-NH_2 \longrightarrow \text{⬡}-N=N-\text{⬡}-NH_2 + H^+$$

phenylamine   yellow azo compound

The uses of azo compounds

The chromophore makes the azo dye coloured – see page 61.

Aromatic azo compounds make excellent fade-resistant dyes. By attaching different functional groups to the chromophore, the properties of the molecule are modified, as shown in the table.

Additional functional group(s)	Property modified	Example
$-SO_3^-Na^+$	The solubility of the dye in water is improved, due to the ionic group – it can form ionic bonds with a protein fibre, such as wool	$H_2N-\text{⬡}-N=N-\text{⬡}-SO_3^-Na^+$
$-NH_2$ or $-NR_2$	The colour of the dye is modified or enhanced	$H_2N-\text{⬡}-N=N-\text{⬡}-NH_2$

QUICK CHECK QUESTIONS

1 Write equations for the reaction of:
   (a) dilute hydrochloric acid with sodium nitrate(III)
   (b) cold nitrous acid with phenylamine
   (c) benzenediazonium ion with an alkaline solution of phenol.
2 There are quite a number of dyes with more than one azo group per molecule. How is this achieved?
3 Modern azo dye manufacturing plants nearly always have an ice-making plant nearby. Explain why.

4 The acid–base indicator methyl orange is an azo dye. It has the structure:

$$^+Na^-O_3S-\text{⬡}-N=N-\text{⬡}-N\begin{matrix}CH_3\\CH_3\end{matrix}$$
methyl orange

Suggest how methyl orange could be synthesised. (*Hint:* use a coupling reaction.)

Chemistry of colour

Chemical Ideas 6.9

Coloured inorganic compounds

Many transition metal ions are coloured because electrons in their **d orbitals** can be excited. When the transition metal ion is surrounded by ligands, the d orbitals are **split** into two different energy levels.

Electrons in the lower of these two new energy levels can be excited to the higher level. The excitation energy required corresponds to the absorption of visible light. Factors that affect the excitation energy (ΔE), and therefore the colour of the complex, include:

- the type of ligand
- the shape of the complex – octahedral or tetrahedral
- the coordination number of the complex
- the charge on the central transition metal ion.

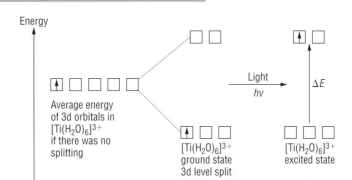

In an **isolated** transition metal ion, all the d orbitals (and any electrons in them) have the *same* energy.

If the d sub-shell is empty, or completely full, then the transition metal ion is colourless.

Coloured organic compounds

The part of an organic molecule responsible for any colour is called the **chromophore**. This is an extended delocalised system of electrons containing unsaturated groups such as C=C, C=O, N=N and benzene rings. Electrons in the delocalised system generally need less energy to become excited than those in single covalent bonds – this energy is available when the molecule absorbs visible light.

Examples of chromophores can be found in azo dyes (see page 60).

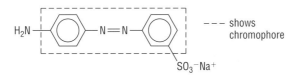

shows chromophore

Examples of chromophores can be found in azo dyes (see page 60).

QUICK CHECK QUESTIONS

1 The complex ion $[Ni(H_2O)_6]^{2+}$(aq) is green in colour.
   (a) Write down the electronic arrangement of the Ni^{2+} ion.
   (b) Explain, with the aid of a diagram, why this complex ion is coloured.
   (c) When the ligand edta^{4-} is added to $[Ni(H_2O)_6]^{2+}$, a blue complex ion forms. Explain why the new complex has a different colour.

2 What effect does extending the delocalised system, in an organic molecule, have on the absorption frequency?

3 Explain why all scandium(III) compounds are white.

4 This is the structure of the dye called 'Acid Orange 7' –

Acid Orange 7

   (a) Sketch the molecule and draw a ring around the chromophore.
   (b) Explain why Acid Orange 7 is coloured.
   (c) Suggest how the colour of Acid Orange 7 might be modified.

The Oceans (O)

The vast expanses of seawater, called oceans, play an essential part in the cycling of many chemicals and also in climate control. This module is about the fundamental chemistry that lies behind these ocean processes. 'CI' refers to sections of your *Chemical Ideas* textbook. 'Storylines' refers to your *Chemical Storylines* textbook.

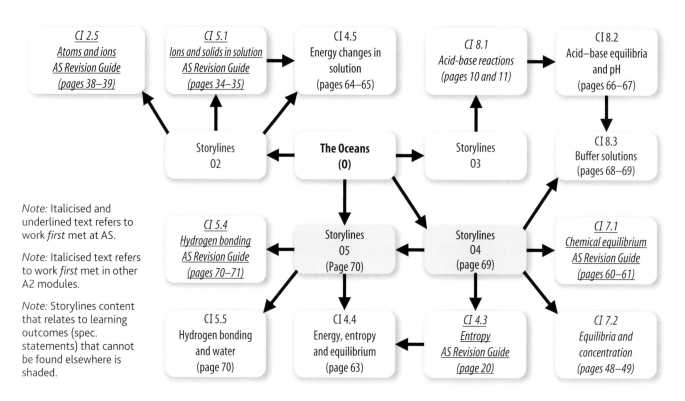

Note: Italicised and underlined text refers to work *first* met at AS.

Note: Italicised text refers to work *first* met in other A2 modules.

Note: Storylines content that relates to learning outcomes (spec. statements) that cannot be found elsewhere is shaded.

CI 2.5 *Atoms and ions AS Revision Guide (pages 38–39)*

CI 5.1 *Ions and solids in solution AS Revision Guide (pages 34–35)*

CI 4.5 Energy changes in solution (pages 64–65)

CI 8.1 *Acid-base reactions (pages 10 and 11)*

CI 8.2 Acid–base equilibria and pH (pages 66–67)

Storylines 02

The Oceans (O)

Storylines 03

CI 8.3 Buffer solutions (pages 68–69)

CI 5.4 *Hydrogen bonding AS Revision Guide (pages 70–71)*

Storylines 05 (Page 70)

Storylines 04 (page 69)

CI 7.1 *Chemical equilibrium AS Revision Guide (pages 60–61)*

CI 5.5 Hydrogen bonding and water (page 70)

CI 4.4 Energy, entropy and equilibrium (page 63)

CI 4.3 *Entropy AS Revision Guide (page 20)*

CI 7.2 Equilibria and concentration (pages 48–49)

From *Chemical Storylines* you will need to know the following.

A safe carbon store (Storylines O4)

Carbon dioxide dissolves in water via the following reactions:

$$CO_2(g) \rightleftharpoons CO_2(aq)$$

$$CO_2(aq) + H_2O(l) \rightleftharpoons H^+(aq) + HCO_3^-(aq)$$

$$HCO_3^-(aq) \rightleftharpoons H^+(aq) + CO_3^{2-}(aq)$$

Adding these gives the overall equation:

$$CO_2(g) + H_2O(l) \rightleftharpoons 2H^+(aq) + CO_3^{2-}(aq)$$
carbonic acid

> By le Chatelier's principle, increasing $[CO_2(g)]$ makes the positions of all three equilibria move to the right.

As human activity increases atmospheric carbon dioxide a range of methods, such as more economical use of fossil fuels, using alternatives to fossil fuels (e.g. hydrogen), capture and storage of carbon dioxide, and increased levels of photosynthesis, have been suggested to improve the situation.

> For each method for reducing the atmospheric carbon dioxide level you need to be able to discuss the risks and benefits associated with it.

Energy, entropy and equilibrium

Chemical Ideas 4.4

Entropy changes

You were introduced to entropy on page 20 in *Revise AS Chemistry for Salters*.

The entropy change for a chemical system (ΔS_{sys}) is the difference between the entropies of the reactants and products in the equation for the reaction:

$$\Delta S_{sys} = \Sigma \Delta S(\text{products}) - \Sigma \Delta S(\text{reactants})$$

The entropy change for the surroundings (ΔS_{surr}) depends on the transfer of heat to/from the surroundings, i.e. the enthalpy change (ΔH):

$$\Delta S_{surr} = -\frac{\Delta H}{T}$$

T is in *K* for entropy calculation
0 °C = 273 K.

Knowing the total entropy change enables predictions to be made:

- if ΔS_{total} is positive then a reaction will occur spontaneously
- if $\Delta S_{total} = 0$ then the reaction is at equilibrium.

WORKED EXAMPLE 1

Calculate $\Delta S^{\ominus}$ for the formation of ammonia, using the data provided.

$S^{\ominus}[N_2(g)] = 192\,J\,K^{-1}\,mol^{-1}$, $S^{\ominus}[H_2(g)] = 131\,J\,K^{-1}\,mol^{-1}$, $S^{\ominus}[NH_3(g)] = 193\,J\,K^{-1}\,mol^{-1}$

$N_2(g) + 3H_2(g) \rightleftharpoons 2NH_3(g)$

$\Delta S^{\ominus} = \Sigma S^{\ominus}[\text{products}] - \Sigma S^{\ominus}[\text{reactants}]$

$= [2 \times S^{\ominus}(NH_3(g))] - [S^{\ominus}(N_2(g)) + 3 \times S^{\ominus}(H_2(g))]$

$= [2 \times 193] - [192 + (3 \times 131)] = -199\,J\,K^{-1}\,mol^{-1}$

There is a decrease in entropy because overall the number of moles of gas decreases.

WORKED EXAMPLE 2

The total entropy change (ΔS_{total}) is the sum of these:
$\Delta S_{total} = \Delta S_{sys} + \Delta S_{surr}$

For ice melting, $\Delta H = +6.02\,kJ\,mol^{-1}$ and $\Delta S_{sys} = +22\,J\,K^{-1}\,mol^{-1}$. Calculate the total entropy change for ice melting at 0 °C and comment on the state of such a system.

$\Delta S_{surr} = -\frac{\Delta H}{T} = -6020\,J\,mol^{-1}/273\,K = -22.0\,J\,K^{-1}\,mol^{-1}$

$\Delta S_{total} = \Delta S_{sys} + \Delta S_{surr} = +22.0\,J\,K^{-1}\,mol^{-1} - 22.0\,J\,K^{-1}\,mol^{-1} = 0.00$

Remember to convert ΔH to $J\,mol^{-1}$ and the temperature to *K*.
0 °C = 273 K.

If ΔS_{total} is zero then ice and water are in equilibrium at 273 K

QUICK CHECK QUESTIONS

1 Why does a gas have a higher entropy than a liquid?
2 Calculate the standard entropy change ($\Delta S^{\ominus}_{sys}$) for the reaction:
$Cl_2(g) + F_2(g) \rightarrow 2ClF(g)$
given that the standard entropies ($S^{\ominus}$) of gaseous Cl_2, F_2 and ClF are +202, +222 and +218 $J\,K^{-1}\,mol^{-1}$ respectively.

3 (a) Calculate the total entropy change for the decomposition of magnesium carbonate at 500 °C. Does the reaction occur spontaneously?
$MgCO_3(s) \rightarrow MgO(s) + CO_2(g)$
$\Delta H^{\ominus} = +100.3\,kJ\,mol^{-1}$
$\Delta S^{\ominus}_{sys} = +174.8\,J\,K^{-1}\,mol^{-1}$

(b) What would be the minimum temperature (to the nearest degree) required for any decomposition of magnesium carbonate?

Energy changes and solutions

Chemical Ideas 4.5

When ionic compounds dissolve in water, the ionic lattice is broken up and the ions separate and become hydrated. Energy is used to break up the lattice (ionic bonds are broken) but energy is given out when the ions are hydrated (ion–dipole bonds are formed).

Lattice (formation) enthalpy

The magnitude of ΔH_{LE} is an indication of bond strength in the lattice.

ΔH_{LE} is the enthalpy change when 1 mole of a solid is formed from its separate gaseous ions. For example:

$$Na^+(g) + Cl^-(g) \rightarrow NaCl(s) \qquad \Delta H_{LE}(NaCl) = -788\,kJ\,mol^{-1}$$

$$Mg^{2+}(g) + 2Cl^-(g) \rightarrow MgCl_2(s) \qquad \Delta H_{LE}(MgCl_2) = -2434\,kJ\,mol^{-1}$$

This involves the **formation** of ionic bonds, and so ΔH_{LE} is **always negative**.

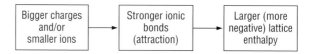

The ionic radius of an element depends on:

*   the nuclear charge (atomic number) – the bigger the nuclear charge, the smaller the ion (for atoms with the same number of filled energy levels)
*   the number of full energy levels – the more levels, the bigger the ion.

Enthalpy change of hydration

ΔH_{hyd} is the enthalpy change when an aqueous solution is formed from 1 mole of gaseous ions. For example:

'aq' represents water acting as a solvent.

$$Na^+(g) + aq \rightarrow Na^+(aq) \qquad \Delta H_{hyd}(Na^+) = -406\,kJ\,mol^{-1}$$

$$Br^-(g) + aq \rightarrow Br^-(aq) \qquad \Delta H_{hyd}(Br^-) = -337\,kJ\,mol^{-1}$$

ΔH_{hyd} values are always negative.

This involves ion–dipole bonds forming, and so ΔH_{hyd} is always negative. The greater the enthalpy change of hydration, the stronger the ion–dipole attractions and the greater the number of water molecules surrounding the ion. The strength of the ion–dipole attraction depends on the charge and size of the ions.

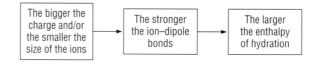

Enthalpy change of solution

Enthalpy change of solvation, ΔH_{solv}, is the enthalpy change when a solution is formed from 1 mole of gaseous ions using a solvent other than water.

$\Delta H_{solution}$ is the enthalpy change when 1 mole of a solute dissolves to form a dilute solution. This can be thought of as a two-step process – breaking down the lattice and then hydrating the gaseous ions produced (water is the solvent):

$$\Delta H_{solution} = \Delta H_{hyd}(cation) + \Delta H_{hyd}(anion) - \Delta H_{LE}$$

If $\Delta H_{solution}$ is negative (see below) or slightly positive (see right), then the solid will usually dissolve because the **entropy change** will be generally favourable.

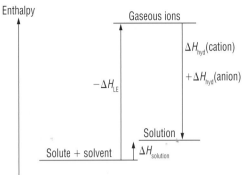

$\Delta H_{solution}$ is small and positive; the solute **may** dissolve

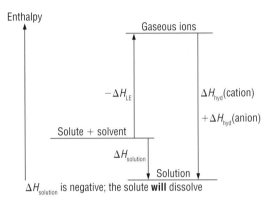

$\Delta H_{solution}$ is negative; the solute **will** dissolve

If $\Delta H_{solution}$ is large and positive (see right) then the solid will not dissolve, even though the **entropy change** will be generally favourable, because too much energy is needed. This is always the case with ionic solutes in non-polar solvents, $-\Delta H_{solv}$ is tiny because there is little attraction between the ions and solvent.

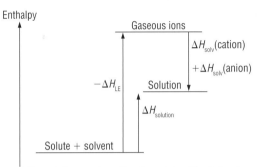

$\Delta H_{solution}$ is large and positive; the solute **will not** dissolve

WORKED EXAMPLE

Calculate $\Delta H_{solution}$ for $CaCl_2$ from the following data. Then predict if calcium chloride is water soluble.

$\Delta H_{hyd}(Ca^{2+}) = -1579 \,kJ\,mol^{-1}$; $\Delta H_{hyd}(Cl^-) = -364 \,kJ\,mol^{-1}$;
$\Delta H_{LE}(CaCl_2) = -2255 \,kJ\,mol^{-1}$

$$\Delta H_{solution}(CaCl_2) = [\Delta H_{hyd}(Ca^{2+}) + 2\Delta H_{hyd}(Cl^-)] - \Delta H_{LE}(CaCl_2)$$

$$= [-1579 + (\mathbf{2} \times -364)] - [-2255]$$

$$= -52.0 \,kJ\,mol^{-1}$$

Because $\Delta H_{solution}(CaCl_2)$ is negative, solid calcium chloride will dissolve in water.

> Breaking up a solid lattice into gaseous ions is the reverse of lattice formation, and so the energy input is $-\Delta H_{LE}$.

> The value of $\Delta H_{hyd}(Cl^-)$ is multiplied by 2 because 2 moles of chloride ions are produced from 1 mole of calcium chloride.

> You may be asked to calculate $\Delta H_{solution}$ and predict the solubility of an ionic compound based on figures given to you.

QUICK CHECK QUESTIONS

1 Draw labelled 2D diagrams of
   (a) an NaCl lattice
   (b) a hydrated magnesium ion.
2 Put the following ionic compounds in order of lattice enthalpy (on formation) from least to most negative: LiF, KF, CaO, CaF$_2$.
   Hint: You might like to refer to the Periodic Table on the inside cover of this book.
3 Put the following ions in order of enthalpy of hydration from least to most negative: Al^{3+}, Na$^+$, Mg^{2+}, Ca^{2+}, K$^+$.
4 Draw enthalpy level diagrams for the dissolving of
   (a) KCl in water   **(b)** CaCl$_2$ in water.
   $(\Delta H_{solution}(KCl) = +33 \,kJ\,mol^{-1}$,
   $\Delta H_{solution}(CaCl_2) = -52 \,kJ\,mol^{-1})$

5 **(a)** Calculate $\Delta H_{solution}$ for AgI from the following data:
      $\Delta H_{hyd}(Ag^+) = -446 \,kJ\,mol^{-1}$;
      $\Delta H_{hyd}(I^-) = -293 \,kJ\,mol^{-1}$;
      $\Delta H_{LE}(AgI) = -802 \,kJ\,mol^{-1}$
   (b) Is silver(I) iodide soluble in water under standard conditions? Give reasons for your answer.
6 **(a)** Calculate $\Delta H_{solution}$ for MgCl$_2$ from the following data:
      $\Delta H_{hyd}(Ca^{2+}) = -1920 \,kJ\,mol^{-1}$;
      $\Delta H_{hyd}(Cl^-) = -364 \,kJ\,mol^{-1}$;
      $\Delta H_{LE}(MgCl_2) = -2493 \,kJ\,mol^{-1}$
   (b) Explain why magnesium chloride is soluble in water.
   (c) Explain why magnesium chloride is insoluble in petrol.

Acid–base equilibria and pH

Chemical Ideas 8.2

Remember H⁺ is a proton. You can use the terms interchangeably.

An acid is a proton (H⁺) donor. In aqueous solution, an acid donates protons to water molecules to form oxonium ions (H_3O^+). These are often abbreviated to $H^+(aq)$.

Sometimes the word 'ionisation' is used instead of dissociation when referring to acids.

Acids vary in strength – i.e. in their ability to donate protons. In aqueous solutions of strong acids, almost all of the acid molecules donate their protons – the acid is said to have undergone *complete dissociation*. Examples of strong acids are hydrochloric (HCl), sulfuric (H_2SO_4) and nitric (HNO_3) acids, e.g.

$$H_2SO_4(aq) \rightarrow 2H^+(aq) + SO_4^{2-}(aq)$$

You were introduced to acids and conjugate acid/base systems on pages 10 and 11.

In aqueous solutions of weak acids, only a small proportion of the acid molecules donate their protons – the acid is said to have undergone *incomplete dissociation*. The strength of an acid depends on the position of the equilibrium. The more the equilibrium lies to the right-hand side, the stronger the acid. Examples of weak acids are carboxylic acids (including ethanoic acid) and carbonic acid, e.g.

$$CH_3COOH(aq) \rightleftharpoons CH_3COO^-(aq) + H^+(aq)$$

K_a the **acidity constant** or **acid dissociation constant**. The greater the value of K_a, the stronger the acid. For ethanoic acid:

Square brackets around a formula means the concentration of whatever is inside the brackets, in $mol\,dm^{-3}$.

$$K_a = \frac{[H^+(aq)]\,[CH_3COO^-(aq)]}{[CH_3COOH(aq)]}$$

When comparing weak acids, which can have *very* small K_a values, the K_a can be converted into a pK_a value for ease of use:

$$pK_a = -\log K_a$$

Calculating pH

For dilute solutions the normal range is 0–14.

pH can be calculated using the equation:

$$pH = -\log[H^+(aq)]$$

Strong acids

Monoprotic acids have one acidic hydrogen – they release one proton per molecule.

Because a strong acid is fully dissociated, we can assume that the concentration of acid put into the solution is the same as the concentration of the hydrogen ions in that solution if the acid is monoprotic.

In example 2, the concentration of H⁺ is twice that of the H_2SO_4 because 1 mole of the acid dissociates to produce 2 moles of hydrogen ions.

WORKED EXAMPLE 1

Calculate the pH of a $0.001\,mol\,dm^{-3}$ solution of hydrochloric acid.

$$HCl(aq) \rightarrow H^+(aq) + Cl^-(aq)$$
$$[H^+] = 0.001\,mol\,dm^{-3}$$
$$pH = -\log 0.001 = 3.00$$

WORKED EXAMPLE 2

Calculate the pH of a $0.005\,mol\,dm^{-3}$ solution of sulfuric acid.

$$H_2SO_4(aq) \rightarrow 2H^+(aq) + SO_4^{2-}(aq)$$
$$[H^+] = 0.005\,mol\,dm^{-3} \times 2 = 0.01\,mol\,dm^{-3}$$
$$pH = -\log 0.01 = 2.00$$

Weak acids

Both the concentration of the acid and its dissociation constant are needed to calculate the pH of a solution of a weak acid because it is only partially dissociated.

WORKED EXAMPLE

Calculate the pH of $0.01\,mol\,dm^{-3}$ CH_3COOH ($K_a = 1.7 \times 10^{-5}\,mol\,dm^{-3}$ at 298 K).

$$CH_3COOH(aq) \rightleftharpoons CH_3COO^-(aq) + H^+(aq)$$

Few molecules dissociate, so we can assume that $[CH_3COOH(aq)] = 0.01\,mol\,dm^{-3}$.

A few protons will be provided by the water, but these are insignificant compared to those provided by the acid. So we can assume for every 1 mole of H^+ present there is 1 mole of CH_3COO^-, so $[H^+(aq)] = [CH_3COO^-(aq)]$.

$$K_a = \frac{[H^+(aq)]\,[CH_3COO^-(aq)]}{[CH_3COOH(aq)]}$$

$$1.7 \times 10^{-5}\,mol\,dm^{-3} = \frac{[H^+(aq)]^2}{0.01\,mol\,dm^{-3}}$$

$$[H^+(aq)] = \sqrt{1.7 \times 10^{-5}\,mol\,dm^{-3} \times 0.01\,mol\,dm^{-3}} = 4.1 \times 10^{-4}\,mol\,dm^{-3}$$

$$pH = -\log(4.1 \times 10^{-4}) = 3.4$$

> The temperature should always be quoted because K_a, and ultimately pH, varies with temperature.

> Learn these two assumptions about weak acids.

Strong bases

The concentration of a solution made by dissolving a strong base in water gives $[OH^-(aq)]$ directly, because it is fully dissociated in aqueous solution.

To calculate $[H^+(aq)]$ using an already known $[OH^-(aq)]$, the ionic product of water is used. Water dissociates slightly:

$$H_2O(l) \rightleftharpoons H^+(aq) + OH^-(aq)$$

$$K_w = [H^+(aq)][OH^-(aq)] = 1 \times 10^{-14}\,mol^2\,dm^{-6}\ \text{at 298 K}$$

> K_w is the symbol used to represent the ionic product for water.

WORKED EXAMPLE

Calculate the pH of a $0.01\,mol\,dm^{-3}$ solution of NaOH.

$$NaOH(aq) \rightarrow Na^+(aq) + OH^-(aq)$$

The strong base is fully dissociated, so $[OH^-(aq)] = 0.01\,mol\,dm^{-3}$.

$$K_w = [H^+(aq)][OH^-(aq)]$$

$$[H^+(aq)] = \frac{K_w}{[OH^-(aq)]} = \frac{1 \times 10^{-14}\,mol^2\,dm^{-6}}{0.01\,mol\,dm^{-3}} = 1 \times 10^{-12}\,mol\,dm^{-3}$$

$$pH = -\log(1 \times 10^{-12}) = 12.0$$

> Show all the stages of your calculations clearly. That way, even if you end up with an incorrect final answer, you may be credited with marks for a correct method.

QUICK CHECK QUESTIONS

1   Calculate the pH of $0.001\,mol\,dm^{-3}$ nitric acid.
2   Calculate the pH of $0.05\,mol\,dm^{-3}$ potassium hydroxide solution.
3   Calculate the pH of $0.005\,mol\,dm^{-3}$ calcium hydroxide solution.
4   (a) Give the expression for the K_a of methanoic acid (HCOOH).

(b) Calculate the pH of $0.001\,mol\,dm^{-3}$ methanoic acid ($K_a = 1.60 \times 10^{-4}\,mol\,dm^{-3}$, $pK_a = 3.80$).
5   Sodium hydroxide solution was added, using a burette, to a solution of methanoic acid, and the pH was measured using a datalogger after each addition.
(a) Write an equation for this reaction.
(b) Name the salt produced.

Buffer solutions

Chemical Ideas 8.3

Buffer solutions are solutions that have an almost constant pH, despite dilution or small additions of acid or alkali. Buffer solutions contain:

- either a weak acid and one of its salts – e.g. ethanoic acid and sodium ethanoate
- or a weak base and one of its salts – e.g. ammonia and ammonium chloride.

You can revise conjugate acids and bases using page 10.

All buffer solutions contain large amounts of a proton donor – that means a weak acid or conjugate acid – and large amounts of a proton acceptor – that means a weak base or conjugate base. Any additions of acid or alkali react with these large amounts (or 'buffers') and this keeps the pH constant within limits.

Take the buffer system comprising ethanoic acid and sodium ethanoate solution as an example. The weak acid (ethanoic) partially dissociates to produce its conjugate base and protons. In this case, the acid is a weak acid, so the position of equilibrium lies to the left:

$$CH_3COOH(aq) \rightleftharpoons CH_3COO^-(aq) + H^+(aq) \qquad \textbf{equation 1}$$
$$\text{weak acid} \qquad \text{conjugate base}$$

The salt (sodium ethanoate) dissolves completely in water:

$$CH_3COONa(aq) \rightarrow CH_3COO^-(aq) + Na^+(aq) \qquad \textbf{equation 2}$$
$$\textit{sodium ethanoate} \qquad \textit{ethanoate} \text{ ion}$$

The mixture now contains large amounts of both ethanoic acid (proton donor) and ethanoate ions (proton acceptor) in solution.

If small amounts of acid are added, the added H^+ ions can be removed by reaction with the ethanoate ions present in large amounts from the salt – the position of the equilibrium in equation 1 moves to the left, so maintaining the pH.

If small amounts of alkali are added, the weak acid dissociates to produce more H^+ ions, which react with the added OH^- ions – the position of equilibrium in equation 1 moves to the right, so maintaining the pH.

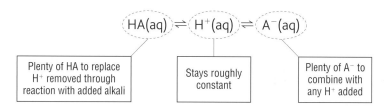

HA(aq) ⇌ H⁺(aq) ⇌ A⁻(aq)

| Plenty of HA to replace H^+ removed through reaction with added alkali | Stays roughly constant | Plenty of A^- to combine with any H^+ added |

Two assumptions are made in buffer calculations:

- all the anions (A^-) have come from the salt, so the contribution from the acid is negligible
- the concentration of the acid in solution [HA(aq)] is the same as the amount of acid put into the solution – in other words, ignore any dissociation.

Calculations with buffers

These all start from the K_a expression:

$$K_a = \frac{[H^+(aq)]\,[A^-(aq)]}{[HA(aq)]}$$

Using the assumptions (left), it can be shown that $K_a = [H^+(aq)] \times \dfrac{[\text{salt}]}{[\text{acid}]}$

Finding the pH of a buffer solution

If K_a of the weak acid is known, along with the concentrations of salt and weak acid, then the hydrogen ion concentration can be calculated – and hence the pH.

WORKED EXAMPLE

Calculate the pH of a buffer solution made by mixing equal volumes of $0.20 \, \text{mol dm}^{-3}$ ethanoic acid and $0.10 \, \text{mol dm}^{-3}$ sodium ethanoate solutions (for ethanoic acid, $K_a = 1.7 \times 10^{-5} \, \text{mol dm}^{-3}$ at 298 K).

By mixing equal quantities, each original concentration will be halved, so:

$$[CH_3COOH(aq)] = 0.10 \, \text{mol dm}^{-3} \text{ and } [CH_3COO^-(aq)] = 0.05 \, \text{mol dm}^{-3}$$

$$K_a = [H^+(aq)] \times \frac{[\text{salt}]}{[\text{acid}]}$$

$$[H^+(aq)] = K_a \times \frac{[\text{acid}]}{[\text{salt}]} = \frac{1.7 \times 10^{-5} \, \text{mol dm}^{-3} \times 0.10 \, \text{mol dm}^{-3}}{0.05 \, \text{mol dm}^{-3}} = 3.4 \times 10^{-5} \, \text{mol dm}^{-3}$$

$$pH = -\log(3.4 \times 10^{-5}) = 4.5$$

> Whenever solutions are mixed, the individual concentrations are reduced in proportion to their volumes in the mixture.

Making a buffer solution of a specified pH

We make use of the general expression:

$$K_a = [H^+(aq)] \times \frac{[\text{salt}]}{[\text{acid}]}$$

The value of K_a determines the pH range for the buffer, and the ratio [salt] : [weak acid] determines the exact pH in this range. So, to make a buffer solution, the most important factor is to choose the weak acid with the correct K_a (or pK_a), and then calculate the ratio of [salt] : [weak acid].

Acid	K_a (mol dm^{-3})	pK_a
methanoic	1.6×10^{-4}	3.8
ethanoic	1.7×10^{-5}	4.8
propanoic	1.3×10^{-5}	4.9
benzoic	6.3×10^{-5}	4.2
chloroethanoic	1.2×10^{-3}	2.9

> $pK_a = -\log K_a$

Buffers in action (Storylines O4)

Carbon dioxide disolved in oceans and limestone rocks (mainly calcium carbonate) act together as the buffering system. The 'carbonic acid' produced (see page 62) acts as a weak acid and the limestone acts as an anion (CO_3^{2-}) sink.

This means that as atmospheric CO_2 levels increase and dissolve to form carbonic acid the pH can be maintained.

QUICK CHECK QUESTIONS

1   Explain what a buffer solution is and how it works.
2   Why does a solution of a weak acid on its own *not* act as a buffer solution?
3   Calculate the pH of a solution containing equal amounts of benzoic acid and sodium benzoate.
4   Calculate the pH of a solution with a concentration of $0.001 \, \text{mol dm}^{-3}$ for ethanoic acid and of $0.005 \, \text{mol dm}^{-3}$ for sodium ethanoate.
5   Calculate the pH of a solution made by mixing equal volumes of $0.02 \, \text{mol dm}^{-3}$ methanoic acid and $0.012 \, \text{mol dm}^{-3}$ potassium methanoate solution.

6   (a) Which weak acid/salt would you use to make a buffer solution of pH 3.1?
        Hint: If the concentrations of acid and salt are the same then $K_a = [H^+]$, so $pK_a = pH$. This allows you to decide which acid/salt system to use.
    (b) What would be the ratio of [salt] : [weak acid] for the buffer solution in question 6 (a)?

Hydrogen bonding and water

Chemical Ideas 5.5 and Chemical Storylines O5

You were introduced to hydrogen bonding on pages 70–71 in *Revise AS Chemistry for Salters*.

The unique properties of water

- Water has a relatively high boiling point for a compound with a low relative molecular mass. See the graph below left, which shows all the Group 6 hydrides.

- Water has a high specific heat capacity (it takes a lot of energy to raise its temperature). Large masses of water circulating in the oceans can carry a large amount of energy and distribute it across the world's oceans.

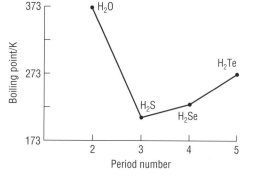

- Water has a high enthalpy change of vaporisation. When water evaporates in equatorial regions, it takes in a lot of energy. When the water vapour cools towards the poles of the Earth and falls as rain, it releases a large amount of energy to the surroundings. In this way, water moderates the extremes of temperatures that otherwise would exist on the Earth.

- The density of ice is lower than that of liquid water. The low density of ice is a result of bond angles – ice has a very open structure, with large spaces.

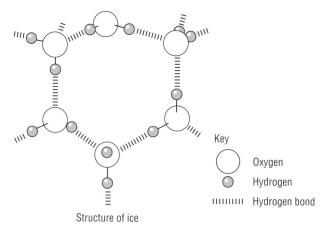

Structure of ice

Make sure that you can draw this diagram showing the hydrogen bonding between water molecules. It should have the hydrogen bonds labelled and show lone pairs and partial charges.

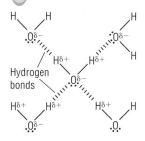

Hydrogen bonding

All these properties can be explained by the strength and amount of intermolecular bonds – hydrogen bonding is the strongest intermolecular bond and water is capable of forming two hydrogen bonds per molecule.

QUICK CHECK QUESTIONS

1 How does a covalent bond become polarised?
2 Both water and carbon dioxide molecules have polar covalent bonds, but only water is a polar molecule. Explain.
3 Explain, using intermolecular bonding, why water has a high enthalpy change of vaporisation.

4 Explain why water's boiling point is much higher than that of methane.
5 Explain why water's boiling point is much higher than that of ammonia.

Medicines by Design (MD)

New medicines have had a major impact on all our lives. This module is about the development and synthesis of more effective drugs. 'CI' refers to sections of your *Chemical Ideas* textbook. 'Storylines' refers to your *Chemical Storylines* textbook.

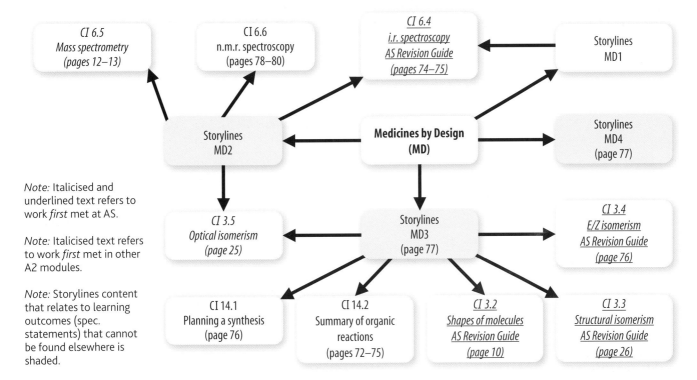

Note: Italicised and underlined text refers to work *first* met at AS.

Note: Italicised text refers to work *first* met in other A2 modules.

Note: Storylines content that relates to learning outcomes (spec. statements) that cannot be found elsewhere is shaded.

This module is very different in structure in that it is predominately **synoptic** in nature – it pulls together many of the ideas and concepts you have come across earlier in the course. The main thrust of the module is to pull together all the organic chemistry from the two years of the course, as well as to look at spectroscopic interpretation, and use this to synthesise and analyse compounds.

Spectroscopic techniques

Each of these techniques provides chemists with different information about molecules. A combination of techniques allows the identification of unknown organic compounds.

Mass spectrometry (MS)

This gives the relative molecular mass (M_r) of compounds. More importantly, the fragmentation pattern provides information about the structural formula.

Infrared (i.r.) spectroscopy

This allows the identification of functional groups because each different bond has a different absorption frequency. So, for example, the homologous series to which a compound belongs can be determined.

Nuclear magnetic resonance (n.m.r.) spectroscopy

This technique allows identification of all the different hydrogen environments in a molecule, and therefore it helps in determining the structural formula.

You will need to be confident in using the different types of formulae – molecular, skeletal, structural, full structural and 3D.

You will need to be familiar with all the different types of isomerism – including structural, *E/Z* and optical.

Revise AS Chemistry for Salters introduced you to:

- mass spectrometry (pages 14–15)
- i.r. spectroscopy (pages 74–75)
- structural isomerism (page 26)
- *E/Z* isomerism (page 76)

A summary of organic reactions

Chemical Ideas 14.2

For each of the following reactions be sure you know the reaction conditions and the reaction type. You also have to be able to write balanced equations for these reactions.

Alkanes

These saturated hydrocarbons undergo radical substitution reactions with halogens.

Initiation
$$Cl_2 \longrightarrow 2Cl^\bullet$$

Propagation
$$Cl^\bullet + CH_4 \longrightarrow {}^\bullet CH_3 + HCl$$
$${}^\bullet CH_3 + Cl_2 \longrightarrow CH_3Cl + Cl^\bullet$$

Termination
$${}^\bullet CH_3 + Cl^\bullet \longrightarrow CH_3Cl$$

Alkenes

These too undergo free radical substitution reactions, but the most important type of reaction for these unsaturated hydrocarbons is electrophilic addition.

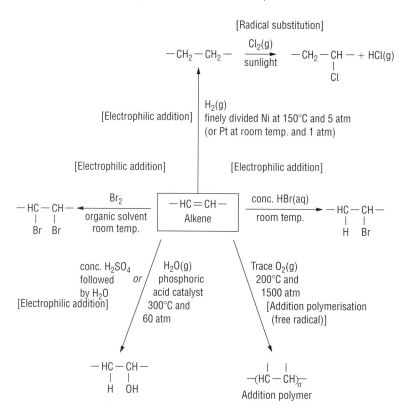

The mechanism for electrophilic addition is:

Note: $Br^{\delta+}$ is the electrophile.

Halogenoalkanes

Because of the electronegative halogen atom and the bond polarity in C—X, nucleophilic substitution is an important type of reaction for these compounds.

The mechanism for nucleophilic substitution in halogenoalkanes is:

Note: OH⁻ is the nucleophile.

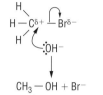

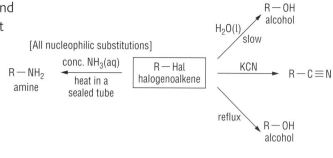

[All nucleophilic substitutions]

$R - NH_2$ amine ← conc. NH_3(aq) heat in a sealed tube — $R - Hal$ halogenoalkene

$R - Hal$ — H_2O(l) slow → $R - OH$ alcohol

$R - Hal$ — KCN → $R - C \equiv N$

$R - Hal$ — reflux → $R - OH$ alcohol

Alcohols

Alcohols undergo several different types of reactions.

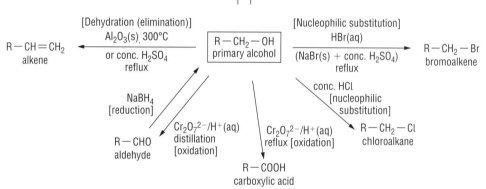

$$R - CH_2 - O - \overset{\overset{O}{\|}}{C} - R'$$
Ester

$R' - COCl$ or $(R'CO)_2O$
anhydrous conditions [acylation]

$R' - COOH$ conc. H_2SO_4 catalyst reflux [esterification (condensation)]

[Dehydration (elimination)]
Al_2O_3(s), 300°C or conc. H_2SO_4 reflux

$R - CH = CH_2$ alkene

$R - CH_2 - OH$ primary alcohol

[Nucleophilic substitution]
HBr(aq)
(NaBr(s) + conc. H_2SO_4) reflux

$R - CH_2 - Br$ bromoalkene

$NaBH_4$ [reduction]

$Cr_2O_7{}^{2-}/H^+$(aq) distillation [oxidation]

$R - CHO$ aldehyde

conc. HCl [nucleophilic substitution]

$Cr_2O_7{}^{2-}/H^+$(aq) reflux [oxidation]

$R - CH_2 - Cl$ chloroalkane

$R - COOH$ carboxylic acid

> Remember that a primary alcohol can be oxidised to an aldehyde (and then to a carboxylic acid), a secondary alcohol to a ketone, but a tertiary alcohol will not oxidise.

> If a primary alcohol is oxidised (rather than the carboxylic acid) and the aldehyde is the desired product, then it needs to be distilled *in situ*.

Amines

The reactions of amines are governed by the fact that they are both bases and nucleophiles.

$R'CONHCH_2R$ secondary amide ← $R'COCl$ [acylation] condensation — RCH_2NH_2 primary amine — HCl [acid–base] → $RCH_2NH_3^+Cl^-$

Aldehydes

The hydrogen atom on the carbonyl carbon atom makes the reactions of aldehydes more extensive than those of ketones.

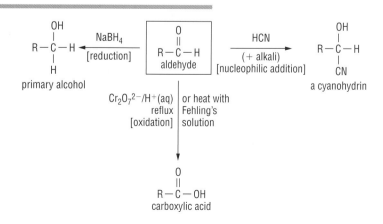

$$R - \overset{\overset{\displaystyle OH}{|}}{\underset{\underset{\displaystyle H}{|}}{C}} - H$$
primary alcohol

$NaBH_4$ [reduction]

$$R - \overset{\overset{O}{\|}}{C} - H$$
aldehyde

HCN (+ alkali) [nucleophilic addition]

$$R - \overset{\overset{\displaystyle OH}{|}}{\underset{\underset{\displaystyle CN}{|}}{C}} - H$$
a cyanohydrin

$Cr_2O_7{}^{2-}/H^+$(aq) reflux [oxidation] | or heat with Fehling's solution

$$R - \overset{\overset{O}{\|}}{C} - OH$$
carboxylic acid

The mechanism for nucleophilic addition in aldehydes is:

$$CH_3-\underset{\underset{\text{:C}\equiv\text{N}}{}}{\overset{H}{\underset{|}{C}}}\!\!=\!\!\overset{\delta-}{O} \longrightarrow CH_3-\underset{\underset{\text{C}\equiv\text{N}}{}}{\overset{\overset{H}{|}}{\underset{|}{C}}}-O^- \xrightarrow{H^+} CH_3-\underset{\underset{\text{C}\equiv\text{N}}{}}{\overset{\overset{H}{|}}{\underset{|}{C}}}-O-H$$

Ketones

Ketones don't have a hydrogen atom attached to the carbonyl carbon atom – they have two alkyl groups. However, their reactions are similar to those of aldehydes, except for oxidation.

$$\underset{\text{Secondary alcohol}}{R-\underset{\underset{H}{|}}{\overset{\overset{OH}{|}}{C}}-R'} \xleftarrow[\text{[reduction]}]{NaBH_4} \boxed{\underset{\text{ketone}}{R-\overset{\overset{O}{||}}{C}-R'}} \xrightarrow[\substack{(+ \text{ alkali})\\ \text{[nucleophilic addition]}}]{HCN} \underset{\text{A cyanohydrin}}{R-\underset{\underset{CN}{|}}{\overset{\overset{OH}{|}}{C}}-R'}$$

The mechanism for nucleophilic addition in ketones is identical to that for aldehydes.

$$CH_3-\underset{\underset{\text{:C}\equiv\text{N}}{}}{\overset{\overset{CH_3}{|}}{\underset{|}{C}}}\!\!\overset{\delta+}{=}\!\!\overset{\delta-}{O} \longrightarrow (CH_3)_2\underset{\underset{\text{C}\equiv\text{N}}{}}{\overset{}{C}}-O^- \xrightarrow{H^+} (CH_3)_2\underset{\underset{\text{C}\equiv\text{N}}{}}{\overset{}{C}}-OH$$

Carboxylic acid and derivatives

The reactions of carboxylic acids and their derivatives are very similar – they differ with respect to equilibrium and in rate. Acid anhydrides and, especially, acyl chlorides are more reactive than their parent acid.

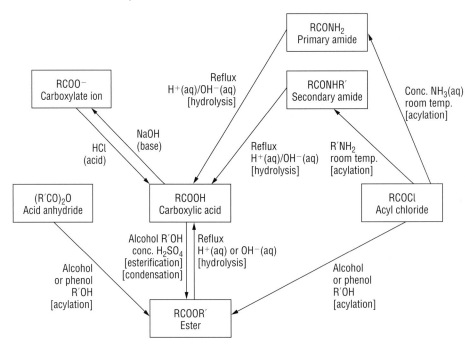

Arenes

The stability of the benzene ring due to delocalisation is an important factor in the reactions of benzene – the most important type is electrophilic substitution.

> All the reactions of benzene are electrophilic substitution reactions, except the addition of hydrogen.

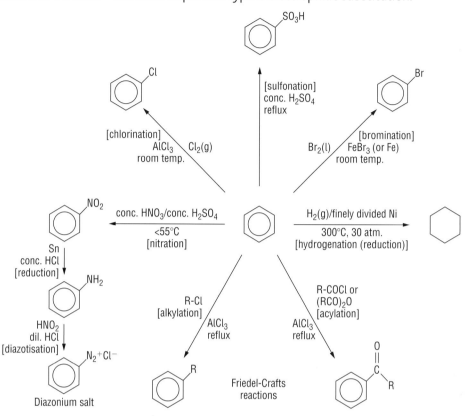

The general mechanism for electrophilic substitution in arenes is:

X^+ = Electrophile   Intermediate carbocation

QUICK CHECK QUESTIONS

1 Draw the full structural formulae for the following and name the functional groups:
   (a) $CH_3CH_2CONHC_6H_5$
   (b) $C_6H_5COOCH_3$
   (c) CH_3COCl.
2 Give equations for the hydrolysis of each compound in question **1**, under acid conditions.
3 Draw skeletal formulae for the following:
   (a) butan-1-ol
   (b) hexanal
   (c) pentanoic acid.
4 Methane can be converted into methanol in a two-step process.
   (a) Name the intermediate.
   (b) Give the reagents and conditions for each step.
   (c) Write equations for each step.
   (d) Name the mechanism for each step.

5 Methylbenzene can be converted into 2-methylphenylamine in a two-step process.
   (a) Name the intermediate.
   (b) Give the reagents and conditions for each step.
   (c) Write equations for each step.
   (d) Name the type of reaction for each step.
6 Give equations for each of the following, stating the optimum conditions:
   (a) the hydrogenation of cyclohexene
   (b) the neutralisation of propylamine by hydrochloric acid
   (c) the dehydration of propan-2-ol
   (d) the acylation of phenol using ethanoyl chloride.
7 Write an equation and name the mechanism for each of the following reactions:
   (a) hexane and bromine in the presence of UV light
   (b) propene and bromine in an organic solvent
   (c) 2-bromopropane and NaOH
   (d) butanone and HCN.

Planning a synthesis

Chemical Ideas 14.1

Combinatorial chemistry is where several similar compounds are attached to solid beads – these are then all reacted with the same reagent in one flask. Several new compounds are made at the same time but are easily separated because they are attached to solid beads.

Starting materials have to be cheap and readily available.

⇒ is the symbol used to indicate a disconnection.

For information on % yield and atom economy, see page 45.

Organic synthesis

New organic compounds are made by a process of synthesis, in which more complex molecules are built up from simpler starting materials. In the pharmaceutical industry, for every drug that becomes commercially available, many thousands of new compounds are synthesised and tested. Variations in the chemical structure of molecules can result in significant changes in their biological activity. Combinatorial chemistry is often employed to prepare these many variations.

The starting point in planning a synthesis is to examine the required (**target**) molecule and its structure. By looking at the functional groups that it contains, chemists can work backwards, using a logical sequence of reactions, until suitable starting materials can be found. This process is known as **retrosynthesis**. Each step in the synthesis will produce an **intermediate** compound.

In order to determine the reagents needed for a synthesis, chemists carry out pen and paper exercises in which they 'disconnect' the target molecule to obtain *synthons*. These are idealised fragments resulting from the disconnections. Each synthon will have a **synthetic equivalent**. Consider the retrosynthesis for phenylethanone (PE), shown right.

There are usually several different routes in a complex synthesis. The preferred route is usually the one with fewest steps. This is not always the case with industrial processes due to other factors – cost of reagents and starting materials, disposal of waste materials and possible health and safety hazards. Other important factors are the overall yield and atom economy.

Getting the right isomer

Some reactions automatically produce a mixture of isomers. This not only reduces the yield, but causes a separation problem; e.g. in the nitration of methylbenzene.

Separating optical isomers is very difficult and time consuming, so the usual method is to start with an optically active starting material, perhaps from a natural source. If enzymes are used to catalyse a reaction, they will be stereospecific, favouring the production of one isomer.

QUICK CHECK QUESTIONS

1 What makes a good starting material for a synthesis?
2 Why are the following important in a synthesis?
   (a) atom economy
   (b) the number of steps
   (c) the percentage yield.

3 Suggest why optically active feedstocks, from natural sources, exist as one enantiomer.
4 Why is the separation of a mixture of isomers difficult?
5 Suggest a retrosynthesis for dimethylamine – include the target molecule, synthons and synthetic equivalents.

The action of drugs
Chemical Storylines MD3 and MD4

Enzymes

Enzymes are proteins that are biological catalysts. They have a particular three-dimensional shape determined by the protein's tertiary structure. The substrate fits perfectly into the active site on the enzyme where they react to produce products. **Competitive inhibitors** have very similar three-dimensional shapes to the substrate and bind to the active site, but do not react. They block the active site so that it is not available to the substrate.

Just as enzymes have active sites, there are many other **receptor** sites in biological systems, particularly at nerve endings. These receptor sites have a specific three-dimensional shape. The natural neurotransmitter not only has the correct size and shape to fit into the receptor, but also forms bonds at several points in order to produce a response. This process is called **molecular recognition**. Chemists try to identify the part of the natural molecule (**pharmacophore**) that produces this pharmacological activity (biological response), so that new drugs can be designed.

Computer graphics can be used to produce a 3D map of the receptor and of promising molecules. Molecules with both the correct shape and orientation of functional groups should be most effective at producing a response. This shortens the time needed to design new drugs. The role of chemists is to help to design and produce new pharmaceutical products, or assist in **computer modelling** for the ethical testing and design of medicines.

> Make sure you know the meaning of all the terms in bold type.

QUICK CHECK QUESTIONS

1 There is an enzyme in the liver which oxidises primary alcohols to carboxylic acids. Explain how administering ethanol to a dog or cat that has ingested anti-freeze (sweet taste) from the road, could prevent the ethane-1,2-diol (active ingredient in anti-freeze) from being oxidised to the very toxic oxalic acid. If untreated the oxalic acid would kill the animal.

2 Penicillin was the first antibiotic produced and is the lead compound for many new semi-synthetic penicillins. The manufacture of new penicillins always has a fermentation stage.
   (a) Suggest why a range of penicillins are marketed by drug companies.
   (b) Explain the meaning of the term *semi-synthetic*.
   (c) It is routine practice to use a low dose of antibiotic in the drinking water of intensively reared poultry, so that they are largely free of infections. Suggest why this increases the chances of drug-resistant strains of bacteria developing.

Nuclear magnetic resonance (n.m.r.) spectroscopy

Chemical Ideas 6.6

Some common nuclei that display this nuclear spin property are ^1H, ^{13}C, ^{19}F and ^{31}P.

What is n.m.r.?

The **nuclei** of *some* atoms have a property called nuclear spin, which makes them behave as if they were tiny **magnets**.

If these nuclei are placed in a strong magnetic field, some align themselves in the direction of the field (like a compass in the Earth's magnetic field) and others align themselves against the field.

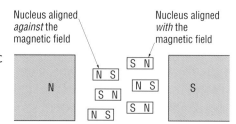

Those nuclei aligned in the direction of the field are at a slightly lower energy than those aligned against the field. If the nuclei are given a pulse of radio frequency (RF) radiation, those in the lower energy state are promoted to the higher energy state – this is called **resonance**. The excited nuclei return to their original state by losing the same amount of energy – this 'lost' energy can be detected.

The n.m.r. spectrometer

If a sample needs to be in solution, deuterated solvents are used, such as $CDCl_3$. These solvents are used because they do not contain ^1H atoms, and so do not interfere with the spectrum produced.

The sample is subjected to pulses of radio frequency (RF) radiation. The energy released when the nuclei resonate is detected and converted to an n.m.r. spectrum on the recorder.

^{1}H-n.m.r. or proton n.m.r.

The nucleus most commonly investigated is that of the hydrogen atom ^1H. When this is the case, the technique is known as ^{1}H-n.m.r. or proton n.m.r. It provides information about the **chemical environment** in which hydrogen nuclei are found. For example, propanone and propanal both have the molecular formula C_3H_6O, but while all six hydrogen nuclei exist in equivalent environments in propanone, there are three different environments for hydrogen in propanal.

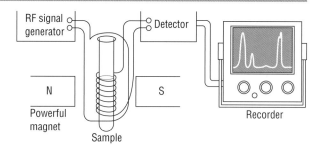

Tetramethylsilane gives a strong, sharp absorption peak with a chemical shift well away from other common functional groups. It is used as a reference and assigned a chemical shift of zero.

CH₃
|
CH₃ — Si — CH₃
|
CH₃

The following are common to all ^{1}H-n.m.r. spectra:

- **absorption** is plotted on the *y*-axis
- **chemical shift**, δ, is plotted on the *x*-axis
- the chemical shift scale runs from 0 ppm at the right-hand side to around 10 ppm.

There is generally an absorption, caused by a compound called tetramethylsilane (TMS), at the extreme right of the spectrum ($\delta = 0$ ppm).

Interpreting low-resolution ¹H-n.m.r. spectra

These are typical low-resolution ¹H-n.m.r. spectra – one is for propanone and the other for propanal.

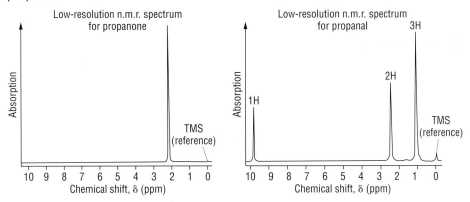

There are three things to look for:

What to look for	What this tells you
The number of absorption peaks	The number of different chemical environments for ¹H in the molecule
The position of the absorption peaks (the chemical shift)	The type of protons, e.g. R–CH₃, R–CHO etc.
The relative area under each absorption peak	The number of equivalent protons in each chemical environment

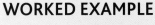

Applying this to the spectra for propanone and propanal:

	Propanone	Propanal
Number of absorption peaks	1 – so one environment	3 – so three environments
Position of absorption peaks	2.2 – indicates R–CO–CH₃	1.1 – indicates R–CH₃ 2.4 – indicates R–CO–CH₂–R 9.8 – indicates R–**C**H–O
Relative area under each peak	1	1 : 2 : 3

WORKED EXAMPLE

The n.m.r. spectra below are for two isomers with the molecular formula C₃H₆O.

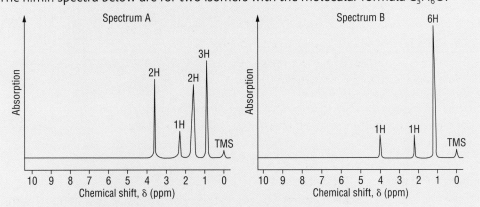

STEP 1: Draw out the possible isomers with the formula C₃H₆O. Identify the different chemical environments for all the hydrogen atoms in each molecule.

Don't look at chemical shift data until you have done this.

You will always be provided with a table of chemical shift values in exams – there is no need to learn this data.

Type of proton	Approx. chemical shift, δ(ppm)
R—CH₃	0.8 – 1.2
R—CH₂—R	1.4
R—C—H (with R above and R below)	1.5
—O—CH₃	3.3
—O—CH₂—R	3.6
R—CH—OH	4.0
R—CH₂—OH	3.6
R—OH	0.5 – 4.5
R—C—CH₃ (=O)	2.2
R—C—CH₂CH₃ (=O)	2.4
R—C=O, H	10.0
R—C—OH (O ||)	9 – 15
R—C—O—CH₃ (O ||)	3.7

WORKED EXAMPLE (continued)

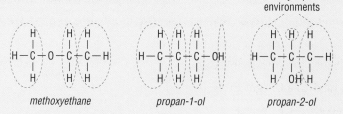

Chemically equivalent environments

methoxyethane   propan-1-ol   propan-2-ol

There are four different environments for hydrogen in propan-1-ol, and three different environments in methoxyethane and propan-2-ol.

STEP 2: Count the number of absorption peaks and identify the number of hydrogen atoms responsible for each peak.

Spectrum A has four peaks. It must be the spectrum for propan-1-ol because this is the only isomer that has four different environments for hydrogen. The number of hydrogens in each environment is in the ratio $2:1:2:3$.

Spectrum B has three peaks and the ratio of peak areas is $1:1:6$. This must be the spectrum for propan-2-ol. It is identified because six hydrogen atoms in this molecule exist in a chemically equivalent environment.

For methoxyethane we would have expected a peak ratio of $3:2:3$.

STEP 3: Explain the position of each peak using chemical shift data.

Spectrum A		Spectrum B	
Propan-1-ol		Propan-2-ol	
Type of proton	Chemical shift (ppm)	Type of proton	Chemical shift (ppm)
R—CH₂—O	3.6	R—CH—OH	4.0
R—OH	2.3	R—OH	2.1
R—CH₂—R	1.6	R—CH₃	1.2
R—CH₃	0.9		

High-resolution ¹H-n.m.r. spectra

A sensitive n.m.r. machine produces a much more detailed spectrum, in which each low-resolution absorption peak can be split into several peaks. Examine the high-resolution n.m.r. spectrum for propanoic acid (right). The solid line indicated the high-resolution spectrum and the dashed line represents the low-resolution spectrum.

propanoic acid

High-resolution n.m.r. spectrum for propanoic acid

3H

2H

1H

TMS (reference)

Chemical shift, δ (ppm)

As before, this arises because each ¹H nucleus behaves as a tiny magnet and it can be in one of two orientations, depending on whether it is in the low or high energy level. Each orientation creates a slightly different local magnetic field. For example, in the CH₃ group there are four combinations of the three tiny magnets:

- all aligned with the external field   S–N S–N S–N
- two with and one against the external field   S–N S–N N–S/S–N N–S S–N/N–S S–N S–N
- one with and two against the external field   S–N N–S N–S/N–S S–N N–S/N–S N–S S–N
- all aligned against the external field   N–S N–S N–S

So the protons on the adjacent carbon atom then experience four local magnetic fields, and so the absorption peak of these protons is split into four peaks in the ratio $1:3:3:1$.

High-resolution n.m.r. spectra are analysed in the same way as low-resolution ones, but provide extra information.

The amount of splitting indicates the number of hydrogen atoms attached to the carbon atoms *next to* the one you are looking at:

- a single is next to a C with no H attached
- a doublet is next to a CH group
- a triplet is next to a CH_2 group
- a quartet is next to a CH_3 group.

> The '*n + 1*' rule gives the number of peaks produced when *n* is the number of hydrogen atoms bonded to a neighbouring carbon atom – e.g. a CH_2 group (*n* = 2) will give rise to 3 peaks in an n.m.r. spectrum in the ratio 1 : 2 : 1.

WORKED EXAMPLE

Look at the high-resolution spectrum for a compound with the formula C_4H_8O, in order to determine the structure.

STEP 1: Find the number of different proton environments. In this case, there are 3.

STEP 2: Analyse the splitting patterns.

δ (ppm)	Group	Peak type	Next to	
4.1	CH_2	quartet	CH_3	} indicates ethyl group
1.3	CH_3	triplet	CH_2	
2.0	CH_3	singlet	C with no H	

> A quartet and triplet close to each other indicate an ethyl group.

STEP 3: Build up the structure of the compound.

The compound is ethyl methanoate.

$$H_3C-C\overset{O}{\underset{O-CH_2-CH_3}{}}$$

δ = 2.0   δ = 4.1   δ = 1.3

QUICK CHECK QUESTIONS

1. How many different absorption peaks would you expect to find in the low-resolution proton-n.m.r. spectrum of:
   (a) methanol
   (b) benzene
   (c) propane
   (d) ethanoic acid
   (e) butanal?
2. What would the relative areas under each peak be for the five compounds in question **1**?
3. (a) Draw the full structural formula of ethanol and identify the different types of proton in the molecule.
   (b) Sketch the *low-resolution* n.m.r. spectrum you would expect for ethanol. Use the table of chemical shifts on page 80 to ensure that the absorption peaks you draw are centred on the correct chemical shift value
   (c) Sketch the high-resolution n.m.r. spectrum for ethanol.
   (d) What extra information does the high-resolution spectrum give?

4. The n.m.r. spectrum below is of a compound with a molecular formula $C_4H_8O_2$. Suggest, with reasons, what the structural formula of the compound is.

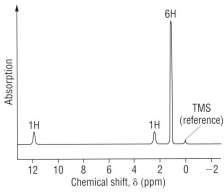

5. Sketch the high-resolution n.m.r. spectrum for ethanal, CH_3CHO.

Synoptic content – using ideas from AS and Unit F334

The table lists the synoptic content which can be examined in F335 examination papers – in addition to that given on pages 44 to 81. If you have forgotten these ideas, or you found them difficult, earlier in the course you should revise them before tackling the practice exam-style questions on the following pages. These ideas will have been revisited in the A2 teaching modules AI, CD, O and MD.

Area of study	Details	Revise AS Chemistry for Salters (page)	Revise A2 Chemistry for Salters (page)	Chemical Ideas (section)
Types of bonding	Ionic, covalent, dative covalent and metallic	8–9		3.1
Representing atoms, ions and molecules in diagrams	Dot–cross, metallic bonding	8–9		3.1
	Shapes of simple molecules (3D representations)	10		3.2
	Structural and skeletal formulae	25		12.1
Properties of ionic and covalent compounds	M.p., solubility in water, conduction of electricity	8–9, 34		3.1, 5.1
	Detail of giant networks	55		5.2
Ions and formulae	Formulae of ionic compounds, oxyanions	12		3.1
	Formulae of oxyanions	40–41		9.1
Ionisation enthalpies	Trends in ionisation enthalpies, position in the Periodic Table and ionisation enthalpies, successive ionisation enthalpies	38–39		2.5
Acids and bases	Brønsted–Lowry theory		10–11	8.1
Electronegativity	Electronegativity, bond polarity and polar molecules	46–47		3.1, 5.3
Intermolecular bonds	Instantaneous dipole–induced dipole, permanent dipole–permanent dipole	46–47		5.3
	Hydrogen bonds	70		5.4
Electronic configuration	Sub-shells and orbitals	44		2.4
Emission spectroscopy	As a basis for laser microspectroscopy	6		6.1
Redox	Oxidation states, half-equations and ionic equations	40–41		9.1
Recognise name and write formulae	Alkanes	24–25		12.1
	Alkenes	25		12.2
	Alcohols	23		13.2
	Ethers	23		13.2
	Halogenoalkanes	48–49		13.1
	Carboxylic acids and their derivatives		2–3	13.3
	Esters		6	13.5
	Phenols		4–5	13.4
	Aldehydes, ketones	72–73	8–9	13.7
	Amines and amides		16–17	13.8
	Amino acids and proteins (recognise only)		26–27	13.9
Reactions types and conditions	Radical substitution (mechanism needed)	58–59	72–75	6.3
	Electrophilic addition (mechanism needed)	66–67	9, 72–75	12.2
	Nucleophilic addition (mechanism needed)		72–75	13.7
	Nucleophilic substitution (mechanism needed)	48–49	72–75	13.1
Isomerism	Structural isomerism	26		3.3
	E/Z isomerism	76		3.4
	Optical isomerism		25	3.5
Instrumental techniques	Mass spectrometry	14	12–14	6.5
	Infrared spectroscopy	74–75		6.4
Entropy	Qualitative treatment	20		4.3
Rate of reaction	Temperature and rate	63		10.2
	Pressure and rate	62		10.1
	Catalysts and rate	64		10.6
Equilibrium	Temperature, pressure, catalyst and position of equilibrium	60–61		7.1
Writing balanced equations	Balancing equations	12		1.2
	Writing ionic equations	35		5.1
Mole calculations involving	Balanced chemical equations	17		1.3
	Masses of reagents	17		1.3
	Molecular formulae	2		1.1
	Percentage yield	52		15.7
	Atom economy	52	7	15.7
	Concentrations of solutions	36–37		1.5
	Volumes of gases	18		1.4

Unit F335
Practice exam-style questions

Note: Each of these practice questions covers a single teaching module (e.g. **Agriculture and Industry**). In your actual exams, each question may cover more than one teaching module. Within a question, the content may be drawn from F334, F335 and in some cases from your AS work. For details of this synoptic coverage see page 82.

Agriculture and Industry (AI)

1   It is possible to produce liquid fuels from methane. This is only really feasible for countries that have large reserves of natural gas. The first stage is the production of methanol in a two-step process.

Step 1 $CH_4(g) + H_2O(g) \rightleftharpoons CO(g) + 3H_2(g)$ $\Delta H = +205\,kJ\,mol^{-1}$

Step 2 $CO(g) + 2H_2(g) \rightleftharpoons CH_3OH(g)$ $\Delta H = -125\,kJ\,mol^{-1}$

Step	Temperature (K)	Pressure (atm)	Catalyst used
1	1050	5	nickel
2	540	90	copper

(a) (i) Describe and explain how temperature, pressure and the presence of a catalyst increase the rates of the reactions taking place in **step 1** and **step 2**. [8]

Use the collision theory in your explanation.

For 8 marks – look for 8 points to make.

(ii) Suggest and explain why the **temperature** used for the reaction shown in **step 2** is lower than for the reaction shown in **step 1**. [4]

(iii) Suggest and explain why the **pressure** used for the reaction shown in **step 2** is higher than for **step 1**. [3]

Use le Chatelier's principle in your answers.

(b) Most of the methanol produced at the end of **step 2** is not used as a fuel, but is converted into a mixture of hydrocarbons in another two-step process.
Step 3 $2CH_3OH(g) \rightleftharpoons CH_3OCH_3(g) + H_2O(g)$
Step 4 $4CH_3OCH_3(g) \rightleftharpoons C_8H_{16}(g) + 4H_2O(g)$

(i) Write an expression for the equilibrium constant, K_c, for the reaction shown in **step 3**. [2]

K_c means the equilibrium constant expressed in terms of concentration.

(ii) Use the data given below to calculate a value for K_c at 600 K for the reaction shown in **step 3**. [3]
$[CH_3OH(g)] = 0.050\,mol\,dm^{-3}$; $[CH_3OCH_3(g)] = 0.20\,mol\,dm^{-3}$

Remember, you need to work out the units for K_c.

(c) Methanol, which is a liquid at room temperature, could be used as an alternative to petrol. However, in the car engine, nitrogen from the air also reacts to form the pollutant gas NO.

(i) Give the systemic name of the pollutant gas NO. [1]

(ii) Draw a dot–cross diagram to show the bonding in a molecule of nitrogen gas, N_2. [2]

(iii) Explain why only a small amount of the nitrogen present reacts in the car engine. [3]

(d) Which of the reactions occurring in **steps 1–4** has the highest atom economy? Explain your answer. [2]

[Total: 28]

Colour by Design (CD)

2 In the late nineteenth century, a new type of dye was discovered. One of these dyes was *Aniline Yellow*.

$$\text{O}-N=N-\text{O}-NH_2$$
Aniline Yellow

(a) State the names of the **three** functional groups present in *Aniline Yellow*. [3]

(b) Chemists also tried to make an orange dye by carrying out a coupling reaction between benzenediazonium chloride and compound A.

benzenediazonium chloride   compound A   orange dye

    (i) Give the reagents and conditions used to make benzenediazonium chloride from phenylamine, $C_6H_5NH_2$. [3]

    (ii) Choose two words from the list below to describe the type of reaction mechanism that occurs when the diazonium ion attacks compound A. [2]
         addition   electrophilic   nucleophilic   radical   substitution

    (iii) The orange dye and *Aniline Yellow* both have the same chromophore. Explain what the term *chromophore* means. [1]

    (iv) Draw the structure of the chromophore that is common to the orange dye and *Aniline Yellow*. [2]

Think about intermolecular bonding.

(c) The orange dye and *Aniline Yellow* can both be made more soluble in water by introducing sulfonic acid functional groups, $-SO_2OH$, into the dye molecules.
Why does the presence of sulfonic acid groups make the dye more soluble? [3]

(d) Compound B is another dye which, under acid conditions, is used to dye wool.

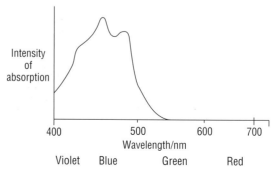
Compound B

    (i) Explain the significance of the 'circle' drawn inside the benzene ring in the above formula. Say where the electrons come from and how they are arranged. [3]

    (ii) Using the diagram (left) to help, draw another diagram to show how compound B attaches to a wool fibre. Name the type of bond that occurs between the wool fibre and the dye. [3]

(e) The absorption spectrum of Compound B is shown below.

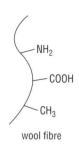
wool fibre

Intensity of absorption

400   500   600   700
Wavelength/nm

Violet   Blue   Green   Red

(i) Use the absorption spectrum to predict the colour of compound B. Explain your answer. [2]

(ii) Explain, in terms of electron energy levels, why compound B is coloured, rather than being colourless. [3]

[Total: 25]

Evidence from the spectrum should be used in your answer.

It would be useful to learn the colour wheel – see page 38.

Colour by Design (CD)

3 In order to restore a painting, it is vital to know as much as possible about the original materials that were used by the artist. Chemists use various techniques to provide this information.

(a) One technique is atomic emission spectroscopy. This can be used to identify the elements present in a tiny sample of paint. Explain how an atomic emission spectrum can be used to determine which pigments are present in a paint sample. [2]

(b) Another technique used is gas–liquid chromatography. This is often used to identify the oils that the pigments are mixed in.

(i) Describe and explain the general principles of gas–liquid chromatography.

QWC: In your answer, you should use appropriate technical terms, spelled correctly. [5]

(ii) The oils in paints are usually mixed esters of propane-1,2,3-triol. Draw the **full structural** formula of a triester of propane-1,2,3-triol. Use R to represent the hydrocarbon chains. [3]

[Total: 10]

Oceans (O)

4 A lake in Sweden was found to be suffering from the effects of acid rain. It was devoid of fish due to the low pH of the water. Sulfur dioxide in the atmosphere was dissolving in the rain and making it acidic.

$$SO_2(aq) + 2H_2O(l) \rightleftharpoons H_3O^+(aq) + HSO_3^-(aq) \qquad \textbf{equation 4.1}$$

$$K_a = \frac{[H_3O^+(aq)][HSO_3^-(aq)]}{[SO_2(aq)]} = 1 \times 10^{-2} \, mol \, dm^{-3}$$

(a) (i) What is the relationship between the concentration of H_3O^+ ions in a solution and its pH? [1]

(ii) A sample of water from the lake was found to have pH = 4. Calculate the concentration of sulfur dioxide in the water. [3]

Work out the $[H_3O^+]$ from the pH. Then use the K_a expression.

(iii) Dissolved sulfur dioxide is a weak acid. Explain what is meant by the term *weak acid*. [2]

(iv) Which species in **equation 4.1** is the *conjugate base*? [1]

Remember *conjugate* indicates product.

(b) In order to increase the pH of the water running into the lake, large quantities of limestone, $CaCO_3$, were applied to the surrounding areas.

(i) Write an ionic equation to show the reaction of calcium carbonate with acid rain. [3]

(ii) Limestone is insoluble in water. Suggest why limestone was used instead of a more soluble base. [1]

[Total: 11]

Oceans (O)

5 The climate of the UK differs from that of Canada, even though both are at the same latitude. This difference is due to the Gulf Stream which carries warm water from the Gulf of Mexico to the western shores of the UK.

(a) Water has a high specific heat capacity and high boiling point due to hydrogen bonding.

> Remember to show lone pairs and partial charges.

(i) Explain the term *specific heat capacity*. [2]

(ii) Draw a diagram to show the hydrogen bonding between two water molecules. [3]

> You should use ideas about relative strengths of intermolecular bonds in your answer.

(iii) Explain why hexane and many other common solvents have much lower specific heat capacities and boiling points than water. [2]

(b) The salinity of sea water depends on the concentration of dissolved salts (mostly sodium chloride).

(i) When sodium chloride dissolves in water, a small drop in temperature can be measured. Copy and complete the enthalpy diagram below for the enthalpy change of solution of sodium chloride. [5]

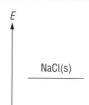

> Remember, enthalpy changes always have a + or − sign in front of the numerical value.

(ii) Calculate a value for the enthalpy change of solution of sodium chloride, using the data in the table. [2]

Enthalpy change	ΔH (kJ mol^{-1})
Lattice enthalpy of NaCl	−788
Enthalpy change of hydration of Na$^+$	−406
Enthalpy change of hydration of Cl$^-$	−364

> Think through whether ΔS_{sys}, ΔS_{surr} and ΔS_{total} are each positive or negative changes.

(c) Sodium chloride dissolves readily in water, even though the dissolving process is endothermic.
Explain why this happens in terms of ΔS_{sys}, ΔS_{surr} and ΔS_{total}. [5]

(d) The oceans absorb large amounts of carbon dioxide from the atmosphere. There is some evidence that the surface waters of the oceans are becoming more acidic. Also, cold water absorbs more gas than warm water, which suggests that as the Earth warms up, the oceans will absorb less carbon dioxide.

(i) The dissolved CO_2 and CO_3^{2-} ions can make the ocean water act as a buffer solution. Explain the meaning of the term *buffer*. [3]

(ii) Describe two approaches for reducing atmospheric carbon dioxide levels.
QWC: In your answer, you should make clear the benefits and risks of each approach. [4]

[Total: 26]

Medicines by Design (MD)

6 The venom of the Brazilian arrowhead viper has been found to reduce the blood pressure of its victim to near zero. It does this by inhibiting a key enzyme (ACE) involved in raising blood pressure. Several polypeptides, which are powerful ACE inhibitors, have been isolated from the snake venom.

(a) Captopril was the first drug designed to reduce high blood pressure.

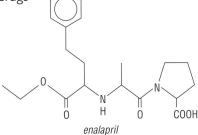

captopril

    (i) Circle an amide group on a copy of the structural formula of captopril. [1]

    (ii) Draw the structural formulae for the two products formed when captopril is hydrolysed with hot, dilute sodium hydroxide. [3]

    (iii) The thiol group, –SH, has similar reactions to a primary alcohol group.

        Choose **one** of the following to describe the type of reaction that would produce an alkene from a thiol.

        addition   condensation   elimination   reduction [1]

(b) Explain how the structures of the polypeptides found in snake venom enable these molecules to act as ACE enzyme inhibitors. [3]

(c) The success of captopril led scientists to develop new drugs to reduce blood pressure.

    (i) Describe and explain the role of chemists in designing and making new compounds for these drugs. [3]

    (ii) Suggest why drug companies produce alternative drugs to treat the same condition. [1]

(d) Enalapril was one of the new drugs based on captopril.

enalapril

    (i) Name one functional group in enalapril, other than the amide group, that can undergo hydrolysis. [1]

    (ii) There are **three** chiral centres in the enalapril molecule. Indicate each of these chiral centres with an asterisk (*) on a copy of the structure of enalapril. [2]

    (iii) Explain why enalapril can exist as *enantiomers*. [3]

(e) A chemist decided to check the structural formula of enalapril by means of its mass spectrum, infrared spectrum and proton n.m.r. spectrum. Describe and explain **one** important feature from each spectrum that the chemist would look for to confirm the structure of enalapril. [6]

[Total: 24]

Medicines by Design (MD)

7 Propanolol was the first beta-blocker drug. Beta-blockers have no effect when a patient is resting, but if the patient is active or excited the drugs reduce heart rate and blood pressure.

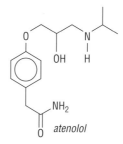

propanolol

(a) (i) Name three functional groups in propanolol. [3]

(ii) Propanolol can act as a base in aqueous solution. Draw a circle around the functional group that enables propanolol to act as a base. [1]

(b) Chemists have worked at producing beta-blockers that are better than propanolol.

(i) Describe two ways in which any new beta-blocker drugs must be very similar to propanolol. [2]

(ii) Explain how computer modelling can help chemists in the design of new drugs. [2]

(c) In attempting to develop new drugs, such as beta-blockers, chemists investigate the effect of introducing different functional groups into a molecule which is known to have the desired pharmacological effect. In one experiment, a chemist introduced an amine group, $-NH_2$, onto a benzene ring using a two-step process.

> You need to learn reaction types, conditions and mechanisms (where needed).

(i) Suggest the reagents and conditions required for the first step of this process, which involves the nitration of benzene. [3]

(ii) What type of reaction mechanism is involved in this first step? [2]

(iii) Name the reagents and conditions for the second step of the process. Use the *Data Sheet* to help you. [2]

(d) Propanolol exists as a mixture of an optical isomer and its mirror image.

> Identify the chiral centre and use this to simplify the molecular representation in order to draw the two mirror images (enantiomers).

(i) Draw three-dimensional structural formulae for the two isomers. [3]

(ii) Suggest why one of the isomers is a more effective beta-blocker than the other. [2]

(e) Atenolol is a third generation beta-blocker whose structure is based on that of propanolol. Atenolol and propanolol have similar pharmacophores.

atenolol

> Look for the common features in both structural formulae.

(i) Draw a ring around the common pharmacophore on a copy of the structural formula of atenolol. [1]

(ii) What type of alcohol group do both propanolol and atenolol molecules contain? Explain your answer. [3]

(iii) This alcohol group can be readily oxidised in the laboratory. Name the reagents and conditions that could be used for this oxidation and name the functional group produced. [4]

[Total: 28]

Answers to exam-style questions

F334 Chemistry of Materials

What's in a Medicine? (WM) Question 1

Page 40

Question	Expected answers	Marks
1 (a)	Primary (1); –OH at end of chain/C with –OH only attached to one other C/contains –CH$_2$OH group (1)	2
(b) (i)	Acidified (1); (potassium) dichromate(VI) (1) or H$^+$/Cr$_2$O$_7^{2-}$ for both marks	2
(ii)	React with carbonate/Na$_2$CO$_3$/CO$_3^{2-}$ (1); bubbles/fizzing/effervescence (1)	2
(c) (i)	Prevents loss of volatile reactants/products	1
(ii)	**One mark each for points in bold** plus one mark for labelled diagram then two other points up to a total of 6 marks: Spot small sample of liquid mixture on (base)line (1); plus small spots of known samples of salicin and salicylic acid (1); on sheet/plate (1); **solvent in beaker below sample/baseline** (1); cover beaker with lid/film (1); leave until solvent front close to top of plate (1); **locate spots with iodine/uv light** (1); **match spot heights from mixture with known samples/compare R_f values** (1) 	6
(d) (i)	 Acyl group shown correctly (1); rest correct (1)	2
(ii)	 Phenol group converted to ester (1); rest correct (1)	2
(e) (i)	138/one with highest m/z value	1
(ii)	Relative molecular mass/formula mass	1
(iii)	C$_7$H$_4$O$_2$ (1); + (1) [allow if structure drawn]	2
	Total	21

The Materials Revolution (MR) Question 2

Page 41

Question	Expected answers	Marks
2 (a) (i)	$$H_3C - \overset{\overset{\textstyle H}{\mid}}{\underset{\underset{\textstyle OH}{\mid}}{C}} - \overset{\overset{\textstyle O}{\parallel}}{C} - OH$$ –OH and –COOH correct (1); rest (1)	2
(ii)	Many monomers add together (to give a polymer) (1); *and* another small molecule/water molecule is produced (1)	2
(b) (i)	C–O bond (1); in the ester link (1) *Must be indicated clearly in words or diagram*	2
(ii)	Hydrolysis	1
(iii)	Products/lactic acid and water (1); are not toxic/occur naturally in body (1) *Do not allow reference to products causing no harm (repetition of question)*	2
(c) (i)	1,6-diaminohexane *Fully correct for two marks, allow one mark if small error (e.g. hyphen/di- missing)*	2
(ii)	Polymer chains can slide over each other	1
(iii)	Poly(lactic acid) has <u>permanent dipole</u>–permanent dipole bonds (1); Nylon-6,6 has hydrogen bonds (1); <u>Intermolecular</u> bonds in nylon-6,6 are stronger than in poly(lactic acid) (1); More difficult to separate chains in nylon-6,6 (1); *QWC mark awarded if terms underlined are spelt correctly (1)*	5
(d)	Five from: filter off white solid (1); dissolve in minimum volume (1); of hot solvent (1); allow to cool and crystallise (1); filter (1); wash and dry (1)	5
(e) (i)	$C_2H_5NH_3^+$(aq) (1); OH^-(aq) (1) *ignore state symbols*	2
(ii)	Bases are proton (H^+) acceptors (1); Lone pair on nitrogen atom (1); Forms dative covalent bond with H^+ ions (1)	3
(f)	Any three from: Minimise hazardous waste during production of raw materials or polymers (1); Minimise energy requirements in production process (1); Reduce carbon emissions during production/use (1); Recycle waste polymer to produce energy or chemical feedstocks (1); Re-use polymer where possible (1) *Allow appropriate alternative answers.*	3
	Total	30

TheThread of Life (TL) Question 3

Page 42

Question	Expected answers	Marks
3 (a) (i)	Moderately concentrated (hydrochloric) acid (1); Heat under reflux (1)	2
(ii)	Ninhydrin (allow iodine)	1

(b)	Primary: order/sequence of amino acids (1); Secondary: folding of amino acid chains/H-bonding between chains forms helix or sheets (1) *allow alternative wording*; Tertiary: folding of protein/overall shape (1)	3
(c) (i)	The two isomers are mirror images of each other (1); which are non-superimposable (1)	2
(ii)	 3D structure correct for one molecule (1); correct mirror image (1)	2
(d) (i)	 peptide link correct (1); rest correct (1)	2
(ii)	–CO–NH– link circled	1
(e)	Proline molecule would make protein chain less linear (1); chains can't pack in a regular arrangement (1)	2
	Total	15

The Thread of Life (TL) Question 4

Page 42

Question	Expected answers	Marks
4 (a) (i)	 Tube containing enzyme and substrate (1); connected with no leaks (1); to syringe or upturned burette in water trough (1)	3
(ii)	The amount/moles of product (1); produced in a given unit of time (1) *Allow 'rate at which reactants are converted into products' for 1 mark*	2
(b) (i)	First order (1); doubling the concentration doubles the rate (1); data used in answer (1)	3
(ii)	Rate = k[hydrogen peroxide][catalase] rate constant shown (1); rest (1)	2
(iii)	$mol^{-1}\,dm^6\,s^{-1}$	1
(iv)	At high [H_2O_2] all the enzyme active sites (1); are occupied (1); Rate depends only on how quickly the enzyme-peroxide complex breaks down (1); *QWC answer makes clear why increasing [H_2O_2] has no effect on rate* (1)	4
	Total	15

The Steel Story (SS) Question 5

Page 43

Question	Expected answers	Marks
5 (a) (i)	(d-block) element forming one or more stable ions (1); which have incompletely filled d orbitals (1)	2
(ii)	Fe [Ar] $3d^6 4s^2$ (1); Fe^{2+} [Ar] $3d^6$ (1); Fe^{3+} [Ar] $3d^5$ (1)	3
(iii)	Having one electron only in each of the 3d orbitals (in Fe^{3+}) (1); is a lower energy arrangement than having two electrons in one 3d orbital (1)	2
(b)	*Answer must be in terms of heterogeneous catalysis*: Transition metals can use 3d and 4s electrons in atoms on catalyst surface (1); to form weak bonds with reactants (1)	2
(c) (i)	$Fe(s) + H_2O(l) + \frac{1}{2}O_2(g) \rightarrow Fe(OH)_2(s)$ reactants (1); products (1); balanced (1); state symbols correct (1) *Allow 2 marks if product shown as $Fe^{2+}(aq) + 2OH^-(aq)$*	4
(ii)	(+)0.84 V	1
(iii)	*Allow one mark for method and two marks for linked correct explanation.* e.g. barrier protection (such as layer of paint) (1); prevents oxygen *and* water (1); reacting with iron surface (1)	3
(d) (i)	Number of moles of MnO_4^- used $= \frac{17.80}{1000} \times 0.0150 = 2.67 \times 10^{-4}$ (1); Number of moles of Fe^{2+} in $10.0 \, cm^3 = 2.67 \times 10^{-4} \times 5 = 1.335 \times 10^{-3}$ (1); Number of moles of Fe^{2+} in $1 \, dm^3 = 1.335 \times 10^{-3} \times \frac{1000}{10} = 1.335 \times 10^{-1}$ (1); Concentration of $Fe^{2+} = 0.134 \, mol \, dm^{-3}$ (1)	4
(ii)	Permanent pink/purple colour	1
(e) (i)	Absorbs green (1); *transmits* complementary frequency/colour/red (1)	2
(ii)	Choose suitable filter/set wavelength (1); Make up standard solutions of coloured solution (1); Zero colorimeter with tube of pure water (1); Measure absorbance of standard solutions (1); Plot calibration curve (1); Measure absorbance of unknown (1); *QWC answer must make clear that sequence of steps leads to being able to read off concentration from calibration curve determined from known solutions* (1)	7
(f)	*Advantages – two from*: Most steels can be recycled; can be sorted using magnetic properties; composition of new steel easily adjusted; scrap steel used to adjust temperature of furnace (2); *Problem*: steel will require cleaning (which adds to costs) (1)	3
	Total	34

F335 Chemistry by Design

Agriculture and Industry (AI) Question 1

Page 83

Question	Expected answers	Marks
1 (a) (i)	Increase temperature (1); more molecules have activation energy (1); when they collide (1); Increase pressure (1); more frequent collisions (1); so more successful collisions (1); Catalyst – provides a different route (1); with a lower activation energy (1) *Allow alternative wording*	8

(ii)	Step 2 exothermic (1); high temperature – position of equilibrium moves left/less product (1) Step 1 endothermic (1); high temperature – position of equilibrium moves to right/more product (1)		4
(iii)	Step 2 – (fewer molecules on RHS than LHS) – higher pressure equilibrium moves right (1); more product (1); Step 1 – (more molecules on RHS than LHS) – higher pressure, less product (1) *If no reference at all to number of product molecules – award max 2*		3
(b) (i)	$K_c = \dfrac{[CH_3OCH_3][H_2O]}{[CH_3OH]^2}$; top line (1); bottom line (1)		2
(ii)	$K_c = \dfrac{[0.20][0.20]}{[0.050]^2} = 16$; correct numbers in expression (1); correct answer (1); no units (1)		3
(c) (i)	Nitrogen(II) oxide/nitrogen monoxide		1
(ii)	$\overset{\times}{\underset{\times}{\times}} N \overset{\times}{\underset{\times}{\vdots}} N \overset{\bullet}{\underset{\bullet}{\vdots}}$ three shared pairs (1); lone pair on each nitrogen (1)		2
(iii)	Triple bond (1); needs a lot of energy/difficult to break (1); few molecules have this energy (1)		3
(d)	Step 2 (1); only the required product is formed – 100% atom economy (1) Alternatively, step 1 (1); both products are useful – 100% atom economy (1)		2
		Total	28

Colour by Design (CD) Question 2

Page 84

Question	Expected answers	Marks
2 (a)	Azo (1); amine (1); arene (1)	3
(b) (i)	(Sodium) nitrate(III) (1); dilute hydrochloric/sulfuric acid (1); <10 °C (1)	3
(ii)	Electrophilic (1); substitution (1)	2
(iii)	Part of molecule responsible for colour	1
(iv)	 *Exactly as shown here for 2 marks; if additional functional groups included max 1*	2
(c)	Ions (1); form ion–dipole bonds (1); stronger or replace hydrogen bonds in water (1)	3
(d) (i)	Each carbon uses three outer shell electrons in covalent bonding (1); the fourth electron is delocalised/shared around ring of carbon atoms (1); region of electron density above and below ring of carbon atoms (1)	3
(ii)	 (1); charges shown (1); ionic bond (1)	3
(e) (i)	Orange/red (1); as absorbs blue/green or complementary colour (1)	2
(ii)	Transition of electrons (1); between electron energy levels (1); absorbs visible light/in visible region (1)	3
	Total	25

Colour by Design (CD) Question 3

Page 85

Question	Expected answers	Marks
3 (a)	Each element produces a unique pattern in the spectrum (1); compare spectrum with those of known pigments to find a match (1)	2
(b) (i)	4 from: sample injected (1); into inert carrier gas stream (1); column/*stationary* phase consists of high boiling liquid on *porous* support (1); detection of emerging compounds (1) compounds distinguished by *retention* times (1) *Plus: QWC mark awarded if at least one of underlined words spelled correctly (1)*	5
(ii)	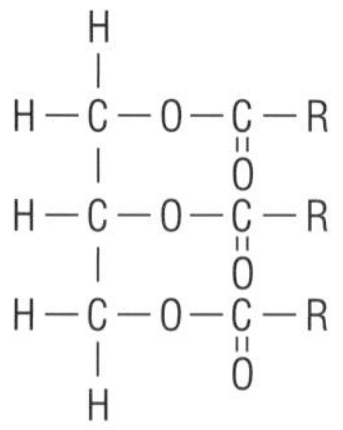 Full structural (1); three-carbon backbone and at least one ester group correct (1); rest correct (1)	3
	Total	**10**

Oceans (O) Question 4

Page 85

Question	Expected answers	Marks
4 (a) (i)	$pH = -\log_{10}[H_3O^+(aq)]$/allow higher $[H_3O^+(aq)]$ = lower pH	1
(ii)	$[SO_2] = \dfrac{[H_3O^+][HSO_3^-]}{K_a}$ $= \dfrac{10^{-4} \times 10^{-4}}{10^{-2}}$ (1); $= 10^{-6}$ (1); units mol dm^{-3} (1)	3
(iii)	Only partially ionises in solution (1); to produce hydrogen ions (1)	2
(iv)	HSO_3^-	1
(b) (i)	$CaCO_3(s) + 2H^+(aq) \rightarrow Ca^{2+}(aq) + CO_2(g) + H_2O(l)$ LHS (1); RHS (1); balanced (1) *ignore state symbols*	3
(ii)	Only dissolves with acid or cannot make the soil too alkaline/too high a pH	1
	Total	**11**

Oceans (O) Question 5

Page 86

Question	Expected answers	Marks
5 (a) (i)	Energy (in J) (1); required to raise the temperature of 1 g of the substance by 1 K (1) *Allow full marks if answer given specifically for water provided not just quoting the figure and units – must be an explanation of the term*	2
(ii)	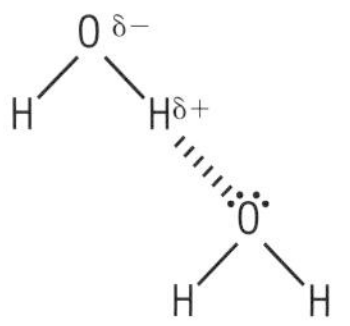 Correct partial charges (i.e. on covalently bonded O–H) (1); lone pair on hydrogen-bonded oxygen atom (1); O–H–O straight line (1) *Ignore additional partial charges and lone pairs*	3

	(iii)	Weaker intermolecular bonds (1); less energy required to overcome/break them (1)	2
(b) (i)		E $Na^+(g) + Cl^-(g)$ $\Delta H_{hyd}Na^+$ $+$ $\Delta H_{hyd}Cl^-$ $-\Delta H_{LE}$ $Na^+(aq) + Cl^-(aq)$ $NaCl(s)$ $\uparrow \Delta H_{soln}$ *Endothermic* enthalpy change of solution shown (1); $-\Delta H_{LE}$ shown with 'up' arrow/ΔH_{LE} shown with 'down' arrow (1); separate gaseous ions shown (1); 'down' arrow with separate ΔH_{hyd} shown for sodium and chloride ions (1); separate aqueous ions shown (1)	5
	(ii)	Enthalpy change of solution $= +788 - 406 - 364 = +18\,kJ\,mol^{-1}$ numerical value (1); + sign (1)	2
(c)		ΔS_{sys} is positive because ions in solution are more disordered (1); ΔS_{surr} is negative (1); because $\Delta S_{surr} = -\dfrac{\Delta H}{T}$ (1); $\Delta S_{total} = \Delta S_{sys} + \Delta S_{surr}$ (1); ΔS_{total} is positive, reaction is spontaneous/takes place (1)	5
(d) (i)		A buffer solution maintains a constant pH (1); even if small quantities (1); of acid or alkali are added (1)	3
	(ii)	Two from: Economise/reduce use of fossil fuels (1); Use alternative renewable fuels (1); Increase photosynthesis/plant more trees (1); Carbon capture/remove carbon dioxide from exhaust gases (1); *QWC: benefits (1) and risks (1) described/explained each approach*	4
		Total	**26**

Medicines by Design (MD) Question 6

Page 87

Question	Expected answers	Marks
6 (a) (i)	Amide link *only* correctly circled	1
(ii)	$HS-CH_2-CH(CH_3)-C(=O)-O^-Na^+$ + (pyrrolidine ring with N-H, $C(=O)$, O^-Na^+) correct bond broken (1); carboxylate anion groups shown (1); rest correct (1)	3
(iii)	Elimination	1
(b)	Polypeptides can fit into active site (1); and form intermolecular bonds with functional groups (1); but don't react/block active site preventing bonding with the desired substrate (1)	3
(c) (i)	Design molecules with similar structures (1); adapt structure so drug more effective/fewer side effects (1); by changing functional groups on basic pharmacophore (1) *Allow alternative answers/wording making similar key points*	3
(ii)	More effective drug/fewer side effects/to give the company a greater share of the market *Allow first or second answers only if not already given in part (i)*	1
(d) (i)	Ester	1

(ii)	three correct chiral carbons (2); two correct (1)		2
(iii)	Chiral centre/carbon means four different groups attached (1); two arrangements possible (for each chiral centre) which are mirror images/enantiomers (1); which are different/non-superimposable (1)		3
(e)	MS – relative molecular mass (1); from highest mass/molecular ion peak (1) or structure by identifying fragments (1); with different masses (1) i.r. – bonds identified (1); each bond absorbs at a different frequency /quote appropriate frequency for the identified bond (1) n.m.r. – hydrogens in different environments leading to structural formula (1); shifts depend on environment/adjoining groups (1)		6
		Total	**24**

Medicines by Design (MD) Question 7

Page 88

Question	Expected answers	Marks
7 (a) (i)	Any 3 of: amine; alcohol/hydroxyl; ether; arene	3
(ii)	Circle round the NH group only	1
(b) (i)	Same pharmacophore (1); same action/effect (1)	2
(ii)	Any 2 of: With an accurate 3D image of the receptor (1); can check whether similar compounds will fit and bind (1); need only make the most promising (1)	2
(c) (i)	Concentrated (1); nitric and sulfuric acids (1); below 55 °C (1)	3
(ii)	Electrophilic (1); substitution (1)	2
(iii)	Conc. hydrochloric acid and tin (1); reflux (1)	2
(d) (i)	 Correct four groups (1); mirror images (1); 3D (1)	3
(ii)	Isomers have a different shape (1); one isomer fits better into the receptor (1)	2
(e) (i)	Should be circled	1
(ii)	Secondary (1); carbon with the –OH (1); is joined to two other carbon atoms (1)	3
(iii)	Acidified (1); (potassium) dichromate(VI) (1); heat under reflux (1); ketone (1)	4
	Total	**28**

Answers to Quick Check questions

UNIT F334: Chemistry of Materials

What's in a Medicine? (WM)

Carboxylic acids and their derivatives

Page 3

1 **(a)** hexanoic acid **(b)** pentanedioic acid
   (c) benzene-1,3-dioic acid

2 **(a)** **(b)**

3 $CH_3CH_2COOH + KOH \rightarrow CH_3CH_2COO^-K^+ + H_2O$

4 Butanoic acid $CH_3CH_2CH_2COOH$ and propan-1-ol $CH_3CH_2CH_2OH$

5 **(a)** **(b)**

   (c)

6

7 Condensation polymer – a small molecule, water in this case, is formed and eliminated when each polymer linkage is made.

The OH group in alcohols, phenols and carboxylic acids

Page 5

1 **(a)** $CH_3CH_2CH_2OH$ **(b)** **(c)**

2 **(a)** 4-methylphenol **(b)** ethanoic acid
   (c) propan-1-ol **(d)** 4-methylphenol and ethanoic acid

3

4 **(a)** A: phenol and ester; B: phenol and carboxylic acid;
   C: hydroxyl
   (b) Order of acidity, with weakest acid first, is C, A, B

Esters

Page 6

1 **(a)** propyl methanoate
   (b) ethyl ethanoate
   (c) phenyl ethanoate

2 **(a)** propan-1-ol and methanoic acid
   (b) ethanol and ethanoic acid
   (c) ethanoyl chloride (or ethanoic anhydride) and phenol

3

   methyl propanoate   *methanol   propanoate* ion

4 An alcohol and a carboxylic acid (or acyl chloride) react together and a small molecule (usually water or HCl) is eliminated

5 **(a)** React the 2-hydroxybenzoic acid with anhydrous ethanoic anhydride at room temperature OR react it with anhydrous ethanoyl chloride at room temperature
   (b) Shake the aspirin sample with neutral iron(III) chloride solution; any purple coloration indicates presence of a phenol group, suggesting not all of the 2-hydroxybenzoic acid has reacted

Which reactions have the highest atom economy?

Page 7

1 Rearrangement and addition reactions have 100% atom economy

2 Reaction A is rearrangement; reaction B is addition; reaction C is elimination

3 Reaction A = 100%; reaction B = 100%; reaction C = 82%

Aldehydes and ketones

Page 9

1 **(a)** butanal **(b)** pentan-2-one **(c)** methylpropanal

2 **(a)** butan-2-ol, $CH_3CH_2CH(OH)CH_3$
   (b) pentan-1-ol, $CH_3CH_2CH_2CH_2CH_2OH$
   (c) propan-1-ol, $CH_3CH_2CH_2OH$

3 You would see
   (a) a colour change from orange to green
   (b) no change, stays orange

4 **(a)**

   (b) Hydroxide ions remove a proton from HCN, leaving CN^- ion which is a good nucleophile

5 **(a)** methanol, CH_3OH
   (b) pentan-3-ol, $CH_3CH_2CH(OH)CH_2CH_3$

6 React both compounds with acidified potassium dichromate(VI) solution – with propanal, there is a colour change from orange to green

   Or, react both compounds with Fehling's solution – with propanal, an orange/brown precipitate is produced

   With propanone there would be no colour change for either test

Acid–base reactions

Page 11

1 (a) acid = HBr, base = NH_3
   (b) acid = H_3O^+, base = SO_4^{2-}
   (c) acid = H_2SO_4, base = HNO_3
   (d) acid = HNO_3, base = CH_3COOH

2 Conjugate acid/base pairs are H_2SO_4/HSO_4^- and H_2O/OH^-

3 An amphoteric substance can act as both an acid and a base

4 (a) acid/base
   (b) acid/base
   (c) redox
   (d) acid/base

Mass spectrometry

Page 14

1 The m/z value for the molecular ion peak indicates the relative formula mass of the compound, because it corresponds to the parent molecule minus an electron

2

Peak at m/z	Ion responsible
34	CH_3F^+
33	CH_2F^+
15	CH_3^+

3 CO_2

4

Peak at m/z	Ion responsible
60	CH_3COOH^+
45	$COOH^+$
43	CH_3CO^+
15	CH_3^+

Molecular ion peak is at $m/z = 60$, which suggests the compound is ethanoic acid, CH_3COOH

5 Compound A must be a secondary alcohol because it oxidises to give only one product, which must be a ketone

Spectrum A

Peak at m/z	Ion responsible
60	$(CH_3)_2CHOH^+$
59	$(CH_3)_2CHO^+$
45	CH_3CHOH^+

Spectrum B

Peak at m/z	Ion responsible
59	Isotope peak
58	$(CH_3)_2CO^+$
43	CH_3CO^+
15	CH_3^+

When propan-2-ol (spectrum A) is oxidised, it produces propanone (spectrum B)

6

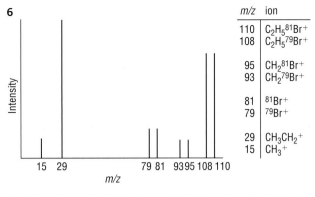

m/z	ion
110	$C_2H_5{}^{81}Br^+$
108	$C_2H_5{}^{79}Br^+$
95	$CH_2{}^{81}Br^+$
93	$CH_2{}^{79}Br^+$
81	$^{81}Br^+$
79	$^{79}Br^+$
29	$CH_3CH_2^+$
15	CH_3^+

7 The peak at $m/z = 62$ is due to $C_2H_3{}^{35}Cl$ and at $m/z = 64$ is due to $C_2H_3{}^{37}Cl$; the ratio of peak height is 3 : 1

The Materials Revolution (MR)

Amines and amides

Page 17

1 (a) methylamine   (b) phenylamine
   (c) propylamine   (d) methylpropylamine
   (e) trimethylamine

2 (a) primary amines = **a**, **b** and **c**
   (b) secondary amines = **d**
   (c) tertiary amines = **e**

3 (a) $CH_3CH_2CH(NH_2)CH_3$
   (b) $H_2NCH_2CH_2CH_2CH_2CH_2CH_2NH_2$
   (c)
$$CH_3CH_2C\underset{NH_2}{\overset{O}{\diagup\!\!\!\backslash}}$$
   (d)
$$CH_3C\overset{O}{\diagup\!\!\!\backslash}\underset{\underset{H}{|}}{N}-CH_2CH_3$$

4 (a) $CH_3NH_2 + HCl \rightarrow CH_3NH_3^+ + Cl^-$
   (b) $CH_3NH_2 + H_2O \rightarrow CH_3NH_3^+ + OH^-$
   (c) $CH_3NH_2 + CH_3COCl \rightarrow CH_3CONHCH_3 + HCl$

5 (a) Products:
$$CH_3CH_2CH_2-\underset{\underset{CH_3}{|}}{N}-H \ + \ HCl$$

   (b) Products:
$$H_3C-\overset{\overset{O}{||}}{C}-\underset{\underset{H}{|}}{N}-CH_2CH_3 \ + \ HCl$$

6 (a) Conditions: reflux with moderately conc. HCl

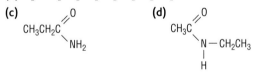
$$CH_3-\overset{\overset{O}{||}}{C}-\underset{\underset{H}{|}}{N}-C_2H_5 \ + \ H_2O \ \xrightarrow{H^+} \ CH_3-C\overset{O}{\underset{OH}{\diagup\!\!\!\backslash}} \ + \ C_2H_5\overset{+}{N}H_3$$

   (b) Conditions: reflux with moderately conc. NaOH

$$\left[\overset{\overset{O}{||}}{C}-(CH_2)_4-\overset{\overset{O}{||}}{C}-\underset{\underset{H}{|}}{N}-(CH_2)_6-\underset{\underset{H}{|}}{N} \right] + 2\,NaOH \longrightarrow$$

$$^+Na^-O\overset{O}{\diagup\!\!\!\backslash}C-(CH_2)_4-C\overset{O}{\underset{O^-Na^+}{\diagup\!\!\!\backslash}} \ + \ H_2N-(CH_2)_6-NH_2$$

Polymer properties by design

Page 18

1 Two different monomers (with reactive groups at each end) join together to form a long-chain polymer; when the monomers react, a small molecule like water or hydrogen chloride is formed

2 In addition polymerisation, only one product (the polymer) is made; in condensation polymerisation, small molecules like water are formed as well as the polymer

3 (a) At 40 °C, PVC is brittle and glass-like – the polymer chains are 'locked' in place and can't slide
(b) At 100 °C, PVC is soft and flexible – the polymer chains can slide over each other

4 (a) Copolymerisation involves introducing a few monomers with bulky side groups to force the polymer chains further apart
(b) Plasticisers act as 'molecular lubricants', allowing polymer chains to slide over each other

5 (a)
(b)

6 (a) Hydrogen bonds   (b) Permanent dipole–permanent dipole

Green chemistry and recycling

Page 19

1 Collection rates are low for domestic waste; domestic waste also contains a wide range of plastics which need to be sorted before being recycled

2 Polymers are broken down into smaller molecules, which can be used as feedstock in the chemical industry

3 Biopolymers, synthetic biodegradable plastics and photodegradable plastics

4 This involves calculating the carbon emissions over the entire life cycle of the material, from obtaining the raw materials to eventual disposal

The Thread of Life (TL)

The effect of concentration on rate

Page 24

1 (a) Measure the volume of oxygen evolved at known time intervals
(b) Measure the amount of bromine produced at given time intervals using a colorimeter

2 First order w.r.t. BrO_3^-, first order w.r.t. Br^-, second order w.r.t. H^+ and overall order 4

3 Rate = $k[S_2O_8^{2-}][I^-]$

4 (b) Half-lives should be in the range 170–190 s
(c) As the half-lives are roughly constant, the reaction is first order w.r.t. the ester

5 (a) Order w.r.t. NO = 2, order w.r.t O_2 = 1

(b) Overall order = 3
(c) Rate = $k[NO]^2[O_2]$
(d) $k = 0.02\,mol^{-2}\,dm^6\,s^{-1}$

6 (a) Both $CH_3CH_2CH_2Br$ and OH^-
(b)

Optical isomerism

Page 25

1 A carbon atom that has four different atoms or groups of atoms attached

2 Enantiomers are molecules that have non-superimposable mirror images

3 Glycine has two hydrogen atoms attached to the central carbon atom; this carbon is therefore not a chiral centre

4

5 (a)
(b)

6 (a) and (c)

Amino acids and proteins

Page 27

1

2

3

4 (a) The order in which the amino acid residues are joined together

   (b) A region where the chain forms a helix or sheet; both are held together by hydrogen bonds

   (c) The way in which the polypeptide chain folds to give its unique shape; this shape is stabilised by intermolecular bonds between the R groups of amino acid residues

5 (a)
Alkaline hydrolysis

$$
\begin{array}{c}
COO^- \\
| \\
CH_2 \\
| \\
H_2N-C-COO^- \\
| \\
H
\end{array}
\quad \text{and} \quad
\begin{array}{c}
H \\
| \\
H_2N-C-COO^- \\
| \\
H
\end{array}
\quad \text{and} \quad
\begin{array}{c}
CH_3 \\
| \\
H_2N-C-COO^- \\
| \\
H
\end{array}
$$

(b)
Acidic hydrolysis

$$
\begin{array}{c}
COOH \\
| \\
CH_2 \\
| \\
H_3\overset{+}{N}-C-COOH \\
| \\
H
\end{array}
\quad \text{and} \quad
\begin{array}{c}
H \\
| \\
H_3\overset{+}{N}-C-COOH \\
| \\
H
\end{array}
\quad \text{and} \quad
\begin{array}{c}
CH_3 \\
| \\
H_3\overset{+}{N}-C-COOH \\
| \\
H
\end{array}
$$

Enzymes and atom economy

Page 28

1 (a) Enzymes only catalyse particular reactions with substrates whose shape allows them to fit the active site
   (b) A molecule with a similar shape to the substrate which binds to the active site and does not react

2 (a) Changes in pH affect interactions between ionisable side chains, which can alter the shape of the active site
   (b) Above a certain temperature, an enzyme's structure begins to break down as intermolecular bonds are broken

3 (a)

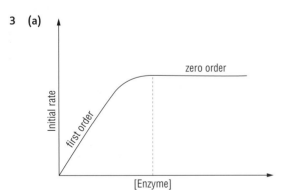

(b) At low enzyme concentrations, all the active sites are full so increasing enzyme concentration increases reaction rate because it increases the number of active sites for reactions to occur; the reaction is first order with respect to the enzyme
   At high enzyme concentrations, not all the active sites are occupied so increasing enzyme concentration has no effect on the reaction rate; the reaction is zero order with respect to the enzyme

4 Enzymes are specific; work well at low temperatures; work well in aqueous solution and offer high atom economy

The Steel Story (SS)

The d block: transition metals

Page 31

1 (a) Ti^{2+}: $1s^2\,2s^2\,2p^6\,3s^2\,3p^6\,3d^2$
   (b) Cr^{3+}: $1s^2\,2s^2\,2p^6\,3s^2\,3p^6\,3d^3$
   (c) V^{3+}: $1s^2\,2s^2\,2p^6\,3s^2\,3p^6\,3d^2$

2 (a) +6   (b) +4   (c) +5

3 Yes because one of its ions (Cu^{2+}) has a partially filled d sub-shell

4 (a) Homogeneous; both reactant and catalyst are in the same physical state
   (b) Cobalt changes its oxidation state (to Co^{3+}, and then back to Co^{2+})

5 Fe^{2+} (green) and Fe^{3+} (orange/yellow)

6 $SO_2(aq) + 2H_2O(l) \rightarrow SO_4^{2-}(aq) + 4H^+(aq) + 2e^-$
   Sulfur(IV) oxide has lost electrons; sulfur has changed oxidation state from +4 to +6; this is oxidation
   $Cr_2O_7^{2-}(aq) + 14H^+(aq) + 6e^- \rightarrow 2Cr^{3+}(aq) + 7H_2O(l)$
   dichromate(VI) ion has gained electrons; chromium has changed oxidation state from +6 to +3; this is reduction

Complex formation

Page 33

1 (a) A molecule or anion with a lone pair of electrons, which forms a dative bond with the central metal atom or ion in a complex
   (b) A central metal ion surrounded by ligands
   (c) The number of bonds formed between the central metal atom or ion and the surrounding ligand(s)
   (d) A bond in which one atom (in the case of complexes an atom in the ligand) provides both the electrons needed to form a covalent bond

2 (a) $\left[\begin{array}{c} OH_2 \\ H_2O\cdots \,|\, \cdots OH_2 \\ Cr \\ H_2O\cdots \,|\, \cdots OH_2 \\ OH_2 \end{array}\right]^{3+}$ hexaaquachromium(III) ion

   (b) $\left[\begin{array}{c} Cl \\ | \\ Co \\ Cl\cdots\,|\,\cdots Cl \\ Cl \end{array}\right]^{2-}$ tetrachlorocobaltate(II) ion

   (c) $\left[\begin{array}{c} OH_2 \\ H_2O\cdots \,|\, \cdots OH \\ Fe \\ H_2O\cdots \,|\, \cdots OH \\ OH_2 \end{array}\right]^{+}$ tetraaquadihydroxoiron(III) ion

3 The chloride ligands cause the 3d orbitals in copper to split; the small energy gap between these d orbitals corresponds to the frequency of blue/violet light, which is absorbed; the colour of the complex is the complementary colour to blue/violet, which is yellow

4 (a) blue   (b) blue/violet
   (c) ligand substitution   (d) $[Cu(NH_3)_4(H_2O)_2]^{2+}$ is the more stable complex

5 (a) $Cu^{2+}(aq) + 2OH^-(aq) \rightarrow Cu(OH)_2(s)$
   (b) $Fe^{3+}(aq) + 3OH^-(aq) \rightarrow Fe(OH)_3(s)$

Redox and redox titrations

Page 34

1 Any two from iron(II) ions, hydrogen peroxide, ethanedioic acid

2 (a) The purple manganate(VII) reacts with iron(II) ions forming a colourless solution
(b) When the first permanent pink colour appears in the conical flask

3 From +7 (MnO_4^-) to +2 (Mn^{2+})

4 (a) 4.48×10^{-4} moles   (b) $0.0896\,mol\,dm^{-3}$ (3 sig. figs)

5 $5(COOH)_2(aq) + 2MnO_4^-(aq) + 6H^+(aq) \rightarrow$
$10CO_2(g) + 2Mn^{2+}(aq) + 8H_2O(l)$

6 A known volume of bleach is added to excess potassium iodide; the solution is acidified with dilute sulfuric acid; the iodine formed in this reaction is titrated against a standard solution of sodium thiosulfate, using starch indicator

Electrode potentials

Page 37

1 (a) $2MnO_4^-(aq) + 16H^+(aq) + 10Cl^-(aq) \rightarrow$
$5Cl_2(g) + 2Mn^{2+}(aq) + 8H_2O(l)$
(b) $H_2O_2(aq) + 2H^+ + 2I^-(aq) \rightarrow 2H_2O(l) + I_2(aq)$

2 (a) Make a Cu^{2+}/Cu half-cell by dipping a copper rod into a solution of $1.00\,mol\,dm^{-3}$ copper sulfate (or other any soluble copper salt) solution; connect this to a standard hydrogen half-cell (298 K, 1 atm) using a salt bridge and a high-resistance voltmeter; take the reading of the voltmeter, noting which half-cell is connected to the positive terminal
(b) Make a Cl_2/Cl^- half-cell by dipping a platinum electrode into a solution containing $1\,mol\,dm^{-3}$ $Cl_2(aq)$ and $1\,mol\,dm^{-3}$ $Cl^-(aq)$; proceed as in (a) connecting to a standard hydrogen half-cell

3 (a) +1.53 V   (b) +0.46 V

4 (a) No reaction occurs
(b) $Cr_2O_7^{2-}$ oxidises Fe^{2+} to Fe^{3+}
(c) $Cr_2O_7^{2-}$ oxidises Br^- to Br_2

5 Oxygen is reduced: $O_2(g) + 2H_2O(l) + 4e^- \rightarrow 4OH^-(aq)$
and iron is oxidised: $Fe(s) \rightarrow Fe^{2+}(aq) + 2e^-$
Hydroxide ions then react with iron(II) ions:
$Fe^{2+}(aq) + 2OH^-(aq) \rightarrow Fe(OH)_2(s)$

Iron(II) hydroxide is further oxidised:
$Fe(OH)_2(s) \xrightarrow{O_2(aq)} Fe_2O_3 \cdot xH_2O(s)$

Where does colour come from?

Page 38

1 (a) green   (b) blue-violet

2 (a) The colour of visible light that is reflected or transmitted; it is the colour we see
(b) yellow-green

3 Electrons are excited to higher energy levels; energy is re-emitted as electrons fall back to intermediate electronic energy levels; energy can also be lost as electrons drop into lower vibrational energy levels

Unit F335: Chemistry by Design

Agriculture and Industry (AI)

Green chemical processes

Page 45

1 A reaction in which one functional group is replaced by another

2 Addition is where two reactants join together and nothing is lost – atom economy = 100%
In elimination, part of the reactant molecule is lost – atom economy < 100%

3 It is very difficult to sort different types of plastic, because they have similar appearances and properties; as a result most recycled plastics are mixtures of different polymers

4 $Ca_3(PO_4)_2 + 3H_2SO_4 \rightarrow 3CaSO_4 + 2H_3PO_4$
310.3 3×98.1 2×98.0
Atom economy $= \dfrac{98.0 \times 2}{310.3 + (3 \times 98.1)} \times 100\% = 32.4\%$

5 The process of extracting aluminium consumes a large amount of energy (electricity) which is largely produced from burning fossil fuels; less fuel is needed to recycle aluminium

Bonding, structure and properties: a summary

Page 47

1 and 2

Substance	Structure	State	Solubility (aq)	Electrical conductivity
vanadium	giant metallic	solid	insoluble	high
xenon	simple molecular	gas	insoluble	low
cotton	macromolecular	solid	insoluble	low
potassium iodide	giant ionic	solid	soluble	low, except (l) or (aq)
propan-1-ol	simple molecular	liquid	soluble	low
steel	giant metallic	solid	insoluble	high
glass	giant covalent	solid	insoluble	low
polyester	macromolecular	solid	insoluble	low
lead(II) nitrate(V)	giant ionic	solid	soluble	low, except (l) or (aq)
silicon carbide	giant covalent	solid	insoluble	low
iodine	simple molecular	solid	sparingly soluble	low

3

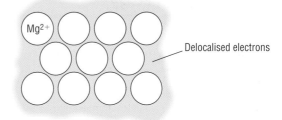

Mg²⁺ — Delocalised electrons

4 (a) Both are molecular and have covalent bonds within the molecule and hydrogen bonds between molecules. Nylon is a very long-chain molecule and the chains can line up – lots of hydrogen bonds between molecules.

(b) Both are molecular and have covalent bonds within the molecule and intermolecular bonds betwen molecules. Hexane has instantaneous dipole–induced dipole bonds and hydrogen sulfide has permanent dipole–permanent dipole bonds.

Equilibria and concentrations

Page 49

1 (a) $K_c = \dfrac{[SO_3]^2}{[SO_2]^2[O_2]}$; units are $mol^{-1}dm^3$

(b) $K_c = \dfrac{[NO_2]^2}{[N_2O_4]}$; units are $mol\,dm^{-3}$

2 $K_c = 2.38 \times 10^{-3}\,mol^{-2}\,dm^6$

3 (a) Increasing the pressure would shift the position of equilibrium to the right; K_c would be unaffected

(b) Increasing the temperature would shift the equilibrium in the endothermic direction – left; the value of K_c would decrease

(c) Position of equilibrium and K_c would be unchanged, but there would be a faster rate of attainment of equilibrium

4 $K = \dfrac{[CH_3COOC_2H_5][H_2O]}{[CH_3COOH][C_2H_5OH]}$

$[C_2H_5OH] = \dfrac{3.0 \times 3.0}{4.0 \times 0.80} = 2.8\,mol\,dm^{-3}$

Equilibrium, rates and industry

Page 50

1 High temperature and low pressure

2 High temperature and catalyst for an adequate rate of attainment of equilibrium; atmospheric pressure is used because increased pressure is not cost effective

3 (a) So that the exothermic reaction takes place and providing energy for the endothermic main reaction

(b) No; position of equilibrium in the desired reaction would shift to left, reducing yield

(c) Low temperature gives the best yield but also reduces rate; compromise at moderate temperature

(d) Dissolve in water

Nitrogen chemistry

Page 51

1 (a) $2NO(g) + O_2(g) \rightarrow 2NO_2(g)$; gas turns from colourless to brown

(b) N from +2 to +4 (oxidation); from O 0 to −2 (reduction)

2 Plough in manure or green manure crop

3 Plant growth (crops) and leaching

4 Nitrifying bacteria carry out oxidation because the highest oxidation state (nitrate V) is produced

Colour by Design (CD)

Oils and fats

Page 53

1 120°

2 Saturated triesters are more linear

3 Because the intermolecular bonds are stronger than in unsaturated fats; this is due to closer and better packing

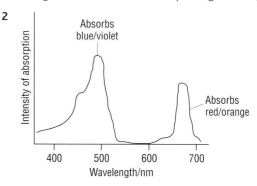

5 Hydrolyse the fat, then acidify to liberate the free fatty acids; produce a chromatogram by g.l.c. and compare with standard traces

6 Each C=C bond reacts with an iodine molecule; the more iodine used the more unsaturated the oil or fat is

Ultraviolet and visible spectroscopy

Page 55

1 The pigment is red; it reflects the wavelengths corresponding to red light and absorbs those corresponding to blue light

2

3 The shade depends on what other colours (frequencies) are absorbed besides red

4 Partially absorbs all frequencies of light

5 Chlorophyll absorbs blue and red light, reflecting green light. (A spectrum is shown as the answer to Question 2.)

Gas–liquid chromatography

Page 56

1 Reduced

2 The relative molecular mass of each component

3 (a) The methyl esters are more volatile than the fatty acids and they will have less affinity for the column; this means chromatograms can be produced more quickly

(b) The relative areas under each peak on the chromatogram are a measure of the concentrations

Arenes

Page 57

1 (a)   (b)

2 Shake with bromine water;
(a) stays orange
(b) turns colourless

3 (a) 6
(b) 10

4 According to the diagram $152\,kJ\,mol^{-1}$

5

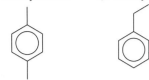

1,2-dimethylbenzene   *1,3-dimethylbenzene*

1,4-dimethylbenzene   *ethylbenzene*

6   A ring of six carbons, with three separate C=C bonds and three C—C bonds

Reactions of arenes

Page 59

1   Catalyst

2

+ 2HNO₃ → + 2H₂O

1,3-dinitrobenzene

Reagents – mixture of conc. sulfuric and conc. nitric acids, warm

3   Add AlCl₃ for chlorine or FeBr₃ for bromine

4

+ 2CH₃Cl → (Anhydrous AlCl₃, reflux) → + 2HCl

+ Br₂ → (FeBr₃) → + HBr

5   three isomers

+ H₂SO₄ → or or + H₂O

Azo dyes

Page 60

1   **(a)** NaNO₂ + HCl → HNO₂ + NaCl

   (b) HNO₂ + ⟨benzene⟩–NH₂ + H⁺ $\xrightarrow{<5°C}$ ⟨benzene⟩–N≡N⁺ + 2H₂O

   (c) ⟨benzene⟩–N≡N⁺ + ⟨benzene⟩–OH $\xrightarrow{<5°C}$ ⟨benzene⟩–N=N–⟨benzene⟩–OH + H⁺

2   Start with di- or tri- aromatic primary amines; diazotise and couple in the normal way

3   The diazonium salt is only stable below 5 °C; adding crushed ice is the cheapest way of cooling

4

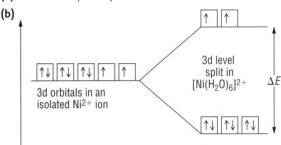

then

Chemistry of colour

Page 61

1   **(a)** Ni²⁺: 1s² 2s² 2p⁶ 3s² 3p⁶ 3d⁸

   (b)

The complex is green because it absorbs light in the red/violet region of the visible spectrum; when the nickel ion is surrounded by ligands, the 3d sub-shell is split in energy; as light is absorbed, electrons are excited from the lower to the higher level; the gap in energy between the two levels is related to the frequency of the absorbed light by the equation $\Delta E = h\nu$

   (c) Changing the ligand changes the energy gap (excitation energy) between the two levels

2   The bigger the delocalised system, the smaller the energy gap between ground and excited states, the lower the frequency.

3   Sc³⁺ has no 3d electrons and so cannot absorb a frequency of visible light

4   **(a)**

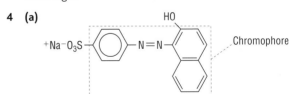

   (b) The molecule can absorb light because it contains an extended delocalised system of electrons; this molecule absorbs blue light, and therefore appears orange

   (c) Functional groups such as –OH, –NH₂ or –NR₂ are attached to the chromophore; this modifies the structure, allowing different wavelengths of light to be absorbed

The Oceans (O)

Energy, entropy and equilibrium

Page 63

1   Gases are totally disordered, liquids have some order; the more disorder the higher the entropy

2 $\Delta S_{sys} = \Sigma S^{\ominus}(products) - \Sigma S^{\ominus}(reactants)$
$= 2 \times (+218) - (+202 + (+222)) = +12 \, J \, K^{-1} \, mol^{-1}$

3 **(a)** $\Delta S_{surr} = -\dfrac{100\,300}{773} = -129.8 \, J \, K^{-1} \, mol^{-1}$;

$\Delta S_{sys} = +174.8 \, J \, K^{-1} \, mol^{-1}$
$\Delta S_{total} = +174.8 - 129.8 = +45.0 \, J \, K^{-1} \, mol^{-1}$
Positive total entropy change; so the reaction occurs spontaneously

(b) For the reaction to just occur,
$\Delta S_{total} = \Delta S_{sys} + \Delta S_{surr} = 0$

$0 = +174.8 + \left(\dfrac{-100\,300}{T}\right)$; $T = \dfrac{100\,300}{174.8} = 574 \, K$

Energy changes and solutions

Page 65

1 **(a)**

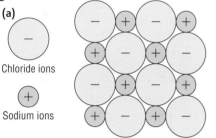

Chloride ions

Sodium ions

(b)

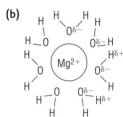

2 Least to most negative ΔH_{LE}: KF, LiF, CaF$_2$, CaO

3 Least to most negative ΔH_{hyd}: K$^+$, Na$^+$, Ca^{2+}, Mg^{2+}, Al^{3+}

4 **(a)**

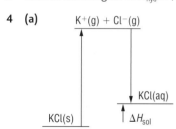

Endothermic

(b)

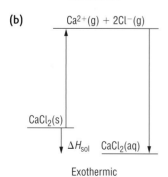

Exothermic

5 **(a)** $\Delta H_{solution} = -\Delta H_{LE} + \Delta H_{hyd}(Ag^+) + \Delta H_{hyd}(I^-)$
$= +802 - 446 - 293 = +63 \, kJ \, mol^{-1}$

(b) Insoluble; $\Delta H_{solution}$ is too endothermic

6 **(a)** $\Delta H_{solution} = +2493 - 1920 + (2 \times -364) = -155 \, kJ \, mol^{-1}$

(b) There is more energy released when the ions are hydrated than is used to break up the magnesium chloride lattice; this is because strong ion–dipole bonds are formed, releasing large amounts of energy

(c) Although ion–dipole bonds would form between the petrol molecules and the magnesium and chloride ions if dissolving occurred, these would be very weak ion/dipole bonds; this is because the petrol molecules (mainly alkanes) are non-polar, so the bonds formed would be very weak; more energy would therefore be needed to break the magnesium chloride lattice than would be gained when the individual ions underwent solvation; this means the process would be endothermic, so would not occur.

Acid–base equilibria and pH

Page 67

1 3.00

2 $[OH^-] = 0.05 \, mol \, dm^{-3}$; $K_w = [H^+][OH^-] = 1.0 \times 10^{-14} \, mol^2 \, dm^{-6}$
$[H^+] = 2.0 \times 10^{-13} \, mol \, dm^{-3}$; pH = 13 (2 sig. figs)

3 $[OH^-] = 2.0 \times 0.005 = 0.010 \, mol \, dm^{-3}$
$K_w = [H^+][OH^-] = 1 \times 10^{-14} \, mol^2 \, dm^{-6}$
$[H^+] = 1 \times 10^{-12} \, mol \, dm^{-3}$; pH = 12.0 (3 sig. figs)

4 **(a)** $K_a = \dfrac{[H^+][HCOO^-]}{[HCOOH]}$

(b) $1.60 \times 10^{-4} \, mol \, dm^{-3} = \dfrac{[H^+]^2}{0.001} \, mol \, dm^{-3}$

$[H^+]^2 = 0.001 \, mol \, dm^{-3} \times 1.60 \times 10^{-4} \, mol = 1.60 \times 10^{-7} \, mol^2 \, dm^{-6}$
$[H^+] = \sqrt{1.6 \times 10^{-7} \, mol^2 \, dm^{-6}} = 4.00 \times 10^{-4} \, mol \, dm^{-3}$
pH = 3.40

5 **(a)** HCOOH + NaOH $\rightarrow$ HCOONa + H$_2$O
(b) sodium methanoate

Buffer solutions

Page 69

1 A buffer solution is a solution that maintains a constant pH despite dilution or additions of small amounts of acid or alkali; it works by having both large amounts of a proton donor and proton acceptor, which nullify small additions

2 A weak acid has a large amount of undissociated acid (proton donor) but a very small amount of the base ion (proton acceptor); the pH will change a lot with small additions of acid or alkali

3 pH = pK_a = 4.2

4 $K_a = [H^+] \times \dfrac{[salt]}{[acid]}$; $1.7 \times 10^{-5} \, mol \, dm^{-3} = [H^+] \times \dfrac{0.005 \, mol \, dm^{-3}}{0.001 \, mol \, dm^{-3}}$

$[H^+] = \dfrac{1.7 \times 10^{-5} \, mol \, dm^{-3} \times 0.001 \, mol \, dm^{-3}}{0.005 \, mol \, dm^{-3}}$
$[H^+] = 3.4 \times 10^{-6} \, mol \, dm^{-3}$
pH = $-\log_{10} 3.4 \times 10^{-6}$ = 5.5 (2 sig. figs)

5 $[HCOOH] = 0.01 \, mol \, dm^{-3}$; $[HCOO^-] = 0.006 \, mol \, dm^{-3}$

$1.6 \times 10^{-4} \, mol \, dm^{-3} = \dfrac{[H^+] \times 0.006 \, mol \, dm^{-3}}{0.01 \, mol \, dm^{-3}}$

$[H^+] = 2.67 \times 10^{-4} \, mol \, dm^{-3}$; pH = $-\log [H^+]$ = 3.6 (2 sig. figs)

6 **(a)** Chloroethanoic acid, and its salt, would be the best choice because its pK_a is closest to the desired pH; fine tuning of the ratio of salt to acid then produces the required pH

(b) pH = 3.1 = $-\log[H^+]$ $[H^+] = 7.94 \times 10^{-4}$

$$\frac{[CH_2ClCOO^-]}{[CH_2ClCOOH]} = \frac{K_a}{[H^+]}$$

$$= \frac{1.2 \times 10^{-3}\,mol\,dm^{-3}}{7.94 \times 10^{-4}\,mol\,dm^{-3}} = 1.5:1 \text{ or } 3:2$$

Hydrogen bonding and water

Page 70

1   When there is a difference in electronegativity between the two atoms bonded together; one atom attracts the bonding pair of electrons more strongly and gains a partial negative charge; the other atom then has a partial positive charge

2   Both contain polar covalent bonds, but carbon dioxide is a symmetrical shape where the centres of positive and negative charge coincide; however, water is a 'bent' molecule, one side has a partial positive charge (H atoms) and the other a partial negative charge (O atom)

3   Water molecules are held together by the strongest intermolecular bonds – hydrogen bonds; two of these bonds have to be broken for each molecule of water before it can vaporise; this requires large amounts of energy

4   Water molecules are held together by the strongest intermolecular bonds (hydrogen bonds), but methane molecules are held together by only weak instantaneous dipole–induced dipole bonds; more energy is needed to separate the water molecules than the methane molecules so the boiling point of water is higher

5   Water molecules and ammonia molecules are held together by hydrogen bonds, but water is capable of forming more hydrogen bonds per molecule than ammonia – two rather than one; more energy is therefore needed to separate the water molecules from each other, so the boiling point is higher than for ammonia

Medicines by Design (MD)

A summary of organic reactions

Page 75

1   (a)

(b)

(c)

2   (a) $CH_3CH_2CONHC_6H_5 + H_2O \xrightarrow{H^+} CH_3CH_2COOH + {}^+NH_3C_6H_5$

(b) $C_6H_5COOCH_3 + H_2O \xrightleftharpoons{H^+} C_6H_5COOH + CH_3OH$

(c) $CH_3COCl + H_2O \xrightarrow{H^+} CH_3COOH + HCl$

3   (a)

(b)

(c)

4   (a) chloromethane

(b) **Step 1:** $Cl_2/h\nu$
Step 2: NaOH(aq)/reflux

(c) $CH_4 + Cl_2 \rightarrow CH_3Cl + HCl$
$CH_3Cl + NaOH \rightarrow CH_3OH + NaCl$

(d) (Free) radical substitution, followed by nucleophilic substitution

5   (a) 2-nitromethylbenzene

(b) and (c)

(d) nitration/electrophilic substitution, followed by reduction

6   (a)

(b) $CH_3CH_2CH_2NH_2 + HCl \rightarrow CH_3CH_2CH_2NH_3^+ Cl^-$

(c) $CH_3CH_2CH_2OH \rightarrow CH_3CH=CH_2 + H_2O$
$Al_2O_3(s)$, 300°C or conc. H_2SO_4, reflux

(d) $C_6H_5OH + CH_3COCl \rightarrow CH_3COOC_6H_5 + HCl$
mix at room temperature and pressure

7   (a) $C_6H_{14} + Br_2 \rightarrow C_6H_{13}Br + HBr$; radical substitution

(b) $CH_3CH=CH_2 + Br_2 \rightarrow CH_3CHBrCH_2Br$; electrophilic addition

(c) $CH_3CHBrCH_3 + NaOH \rightarrow CH_3CHOHCH_3 + NaBr$
nucleophilic substitution

(d) $CH_3COCH_2CH_3 + HCN \rightarrow CH_3C(CN)OHCH_3$
nucleophilic addition

Planning a synthesis

Page 76

1   Cheap and readily available

2   (a) The higher the atom economy, the less waste product is produced

(b) The fewer steps, the simpler the process

(c) The lower the yield, the less product is made and the more by-products are produced; separation of product becomes more difficult

3   Naturally occurring optical isomers have usually been produced at an enzyme's active site, which has a precise shape; this only allows one isomer to be produced

4   The isomers will have very similar properties e.g. boiling point

5

The action of drugs

Page 77

1 Ethanol will be a competitive inhibitor and will block the active site of the enzyme; the ethane-1,2-diol will have time to be excreted and no toxic product is produced

2 (a) Different penicillins have different properties; this allows the doctor to choose the best for a particular infection
   (b) This means the feedstock is a natural penicillin; the structure is altered by chemical reactions while maintaining the pharmacophore
   (c) Using a very low dose means not all the bacteria are killed; the most resistant will survive and become an antibiotic-resistant strain

Nuclear magnetic resonance (n.m.r.) spectroscopy

Page 81

1 and 2 (a) Two peaks with areas in the ratio 3:1
   (b) One peak only
   (c) Two peaks with areas in the ratio 3:1
   (d) Two peaks with areas in the ratio 3:1
   (e) Four peaks with areas in the ratio 3:2:2:1

3 (a)

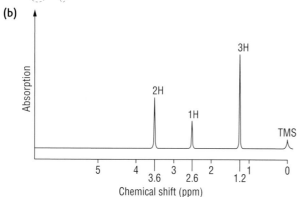

   (b)

(c)

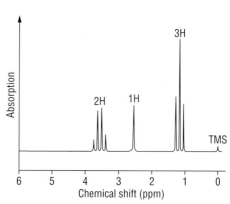

Note: from the reference data given on page 80, you might have given your 1H peak anywhere between 0.5 and 4.5
   (d) There is an ethyl (CH₃–CH₂–) group present

4 The molecular formula could be that of an ester or a carboxylic acid; the absorption peak at chemical shift 11.8 suggests the molecule is an acid; the peak at chemical shift 1.2 suggests there are two methyl groups in the molecule; the molecule is 2-methylpropanoic acid

5

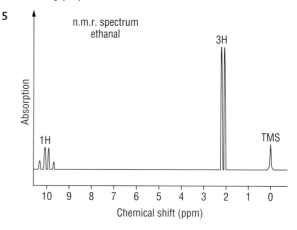

Index